ANIMAL LIFE OF THE GALAPAGOS

ANIMAL LIFE
OF THE
GALAPAGOS

*An illustrated
guide for visitors*

by

NORMAN HICKIN

*With special information
for the visitor*

by
JULIAN FITTER

*With over a hundred black and white
drawings by the Author*

EDICIONES LIBRI MUNDI
Quito

© Norman Hickin 1979

ISBN 0 906604 05 2

Set in 11 on 12 pt Sabon and printed in Great Britain by
Butler & Tanner Ltd, Frome and London, for Ferendune
Books, Regal Way, Faringdon, Oxon. SN7 7DR

Published by Ferendune Books
in association with Springwood Books Ltd.
Published in Ecuador by Libri Mundi,
Juan León Mura 851, Quito/Ecuador,
P.O. Box 3029

To
EMMA
who suggested that I sailed around the
Galapagos in the schooner
Golden Cachalot

Books by Norman Hickin

CADDIS—Field Study Books
WOODWORM—ITS BIOLOGY AND EXTERMINATION
THE INSECT FACTOR IN WOOD DECAY
THE WOODWORM PROBLEM
THE DRY ROT PROBLEM
HOUSEHOLD INSECT PESTS
FOREST REFRESHED
THE CONSERVATION OF BUILDING TIMBERS
CADDIS LARVAE
AFRICAN NOTEBOOK
TERMITES—A WORLD PROBLEM
BIRD NEST-BOXING
WOOD PRESERVATION—A GUIDE TO THE MEANING OF TERMS
NATURAL HISTORY OF AN ENGLISH FOREST
BEACHCOMBING FOR BEGINNERS

Contents

		page
	List of Illustrations	9
	Acknowledgements	12
	Introduction	13
1	History of the Archipelago	15
2	Land Mammals	23
3	Sea Lions and Seals	28
4	Whales and Dolphins	36
5	Land Birds	48
6	Birds of Sea and Shore	66
7	Migrant Birds	90
8	Reptiles	97
9	Fish	118
10	Insects	141
11	Other Invertebrates	197
12	Notes for the Visitor	218
	Further Reading	228
	Index	231

List of Illustrations

	page
The bull Sea Lion, *Zalophus californianus wollebackii*	29
Skull of the male Galapagos Sea Lion	30
The cow Sea Lion, *Zalophus californianus wollebackii*	31
Skull of the female Galapagos Sea Lion	32
The Galapagos Fur Seal, *Arctocephalus australis galapagoensis*	34
The Common Rorqual, *Balaenoptera physalis*	38
The Sei Whale, *Balaenoptera borealis*	39
The Sperm Whale, *Physeter catodon*	41
The Killer Whale, *Orcinus orca*	42
The Bottle-nosed Dolphin, *Tursiops truncatus*	44
The Common Dolphin, *Delphinus delphis*	45
Skull of Common Dolphin	46
American Flamingo, *Phoenicopterus ruber*	49
Galapagos Hawk, *Buteo galapagoensis*	51
Galapagos Dove, *Zenaida galapagoensis*	52
Mocking Bird, *Nesomimus*	54
Vermilion Flycatcher, *Pyrocephalus rubinus*	56
Yellow Warbler, *Dendroica petechia*	57
Short-eared Owl, *Asio flammeus*	58
White-cheeked or Bahama Pintail Duck, *Anas bahamensis*	62

(1) Large Ground Finch, *Geospiza magnirostris*; (2) Medium Ground Finch, *Geospiza fortis*; (3) Small Gound Finch, *Geospiza fulginosa*; (4) Warbler Finch, *Certhidea olivacea*; (5) Large Cactus Ground Finch, *Geospiza conirostris*; (6) Cactus Ground Finch, *Geospiza scandens*; (7) Sharp-billed Ground Finch, *Geospiza difficilis*; (8) Woodpecker Finch, *Cactospiza pallida*; (9) Vegetarian Finch, *Platyspiza crassirostris*; (10) Mangrove Finch, *Cactospiza heliobates*; (11) Medium Tree Finch, *Camarhynchus pauper*; (12) Large Tree Finch, *Camarhynchus psittacula*; (13) Small Tree Finch, *Camarhynchus parvulus* — 63

Waved Albatross, *Diomedea irrorata*   67
Great Frigate Bird, *Fregata minor*, female   69
Blue-footed Booby, *Sula nebouxii*   71
Masked Booby, *Sula dactylatra*   73
Red-billed Tropic Bird, *Phaeton aethereus*   75
Flightless Cormorant, *Nannopterum harrisi*   76
Galapagos Penguin, *Spheniscus mendiculus*   78
Skull of Galapagos Penguin   79
Swallow-tailed Gull, *Greagus furcatus*   82
Brown Pelican, *Pelicanus occidentalis*   84
Yellow-crowned Night Heron, *Nyctanassa violacea*   88
Dome-shaped race of tortoise   99
Saddle-shaped race of Giant Tortoise, *Geochelone elephantopus*   103
Green Turtle, *Chelonia mydas*   104
Skull of Green Turtle, *Chelonia mydas*   106
Land Iguana, *Conolophus subcristatus*   107
Head of Land Iguana, *Conolophus subcristatus*   108
Marine Iguana, *Amblyrhynchus cristatus*   110
Head of Marine Isp, na, *Amblyrhynchus cristatus*   111
Lava Lizard, *Tropidurus* spp. male   114
Lava Lizard, *Tropidurus* spp. female   115
Black-finned Reef Shark, *Carcharhinus maculipinnis*   119
White-tipped Reef Shark, *Carcharhinus albimarginatus*   120
Hammerhead Shark, *Sphyrna lewini*   122
Spotted Eagle-ray, *Aetobatus narinari*   124
Giant Devil-fish, *Manta birostris*   126
Puffer Fish, *Chilomyctenus* sp   127
Sun-fish, *Mola mola*   128
Surgeon-fish, *Prionurus laticlavius*   130
Trigger-fish, *Melichthys ringens*   131
Butterfly-fish, *Holacanthus passer*   133
Pilot-fish, *Naucrates ductor*   134
Side view of the Remora, *Echeneis naucrates*   135
Suction disc of Remora, *Echeneis naucrates*   136
Bat-fish, *Ogcocephalus darwini*   138
Side view of Bat-fish, *Ogcocephalus darwini*   139
Medium-sized locust, *Schistocerca melanocera*   145
Long-horned Grasshopper, *Neoconocephalus triops*   146
Long-horned Grasshopper, *Liparoscelis cooksoni*   147
Widely-distributed cricket, *Gryllus assimilis*   148
Medium-sized cockroach, *Phaetalia pallida*   150
Praying Mantis, *Galapagia solitaria*   151
Termite, *Cryptotermes brevis*   153

Bird Louse, *Pectinopygus nannopteri* 155
Pscocid, *Myopsocus chelatus* 156
Sea-skater, *Halobates micans* 158
Galapagos Sulphur Butterfly, *Phoebis sennae marcellina*, female 160
Galapagos Fritillary, *Agraulis vanillae galapagensis* 161
The Virginian Cynthia Butterfly, *Cynthia virginiensis* 164
The Four-spotted Cynthia Butterfly, *Cynthia carye* 165
Monarch Butterfly, *Danaus plexippus* 166
Queen Butterfly, *Danaus gilippus* 167
Galapagos Blue Butterfly, *Leptotes parrhasoides* 168
Large-tailed Skipper Butterfly, *Urbanus dorantes galapagensis* 170
Hawk Moth, *Hyles lineata florilega* 172
Carmine Hawk Moth, *Agrius cingulatus* 173
Hawk Moth, *Manduca rustica galapagensis* 174
Hawk Moth, *Erinnys ello encantada* 175
Crimson Speckled Footman Moth, *Utetheisa ornatrix* 177
Noctuid Moth, *Melipotis indomita* 178
Noctuid Moth, *Melipotis harrisoni* 179
Noctuid Moth, *Zale obsita* 180
Geometrid Moth, *Oxydia lignata*, female; Geometrid Moth, *Oxydia lignata*, male; Geometrid Moth, *Oxydia lignata*, male 182
Tiger Beetle, *Cicindela galapagoensis* 184
Carabid, *Calasoma galapageium* 185
Cerambycid Beetle, *Estola galapagoensis* 188
Cerambycid Beetle, *Leptostylus galapagoensis* 190
Cerambycid Beetle, *Acanthoderes galapagoensis* 191
Dark-coloured Weevil, *Gersteckeria galapagoensis* 192
Many-armed Sunstar, *Heliaster cunningii* 198
Spiny Sunstar, *Nidorellia armata* 199
Club-spined Sea Urchin, *Eucidaris thouarsii* 200
Sea-biscuit, *Encope micropora* 202
Clypeaster rotundus 203
Sea Urchin, *Lytechinus semituberculatus* 204
Chiton goodalli 205
Masked Flat Snail, *Thais planospira* 207
Cone-shell, *Conus dali* 209
Sally Lightfoot Crab, *Grapsus grapsus* 211
Triops longicaudatus 213
Brine Shrimp of the genus *Cheirocephalus* 214
Web-spinning Spider, *Gasteracantha* 216

Acknowledgements

I feel that I should first acknowledge the help given to me by Richard Foster, captain of the schooner *Golden Cachalot*, and Soames Summerhayes and the crew, in sailing me around the Galapagos, putting me ashore and ensuring that I was able to observe the animal life of the islands. I am deeply grateful to them. Several departments of the British Museum (NH) lent me specimens, made identifications or helped me in various ways, and especially I would like to thank Miss A. M. Clark; Dr T. Clay; A. H. Hayes; G. Howes; Dr R. W. Ingle; Dr D. R. Ragge; Dr A. L. Rice; Dr W. Sands; K. G. V. Smith; R. I. Vane Wright, and P. J. Whitehead.

G. T. Corley Smith of the Charles Darwin Foundation for the Galapagos Isles, gave me much advice on conservation and scientific work in the Archipelago and lent me many papers.

Hilda Maxwell has produced the typescript deciphered from my terrible handwriting on the backs of postcards, and Robin Edwards, in the midst of all his own reading and writing on things entomological and zoological, has found time to go through my manuscript.

Finally Pamela Guilder-Willis, my Personal Assistant, gave unstinted service in putting the book together, making it readable, and conducting correspondence about the book, with my many friends throughout the world.

To all these I give my grateful thanks.

Introduction

The Galapagos Islands lie on the equator some 900 km (600 miles) in the Pacific Ocean from the coast of Ecuador, by which country they are administered. There are thirteen larger islands and innumerable smaller ones scattered over a large area. For the most part barren and inhospitable, these islands support a unique flora and fauna and have served as hiding places for buccaneers, as a victualling centre for whaling ships and as a landfall for ocean-going yachtsmen.

The exact processes by means of which the Galapagos Islands came into being must be attended by a certain amount of conjecture, but it is virtually certain that they have never been part of a continental landmass, such as the nearest one, South America. They have been formed—or, perhaps more accurately, are being formed—by volcanic action. Very active and severe eruptions have taken place in recent years and are certain to continue at various times in the future. At the same time there has been a certain amount of uplifting—a band of fossil-bearing rock high up on a cliff-face near Baltra, bears witness to this. There has been controversy as to the date when the first volcanic island appeared above the sea, but the estimate of the grestest age is put at only ten million years. Other authorities have put their age at considerably less.

Those plants and animals that are now there have found their way by flight or by drifting on the ocean surface, assisted or unassisted by human agencies. Some came on warm water from the north and some on cold from the Antarctic. In the absence of predators, large populations of Giant Tortoises and lizards were built up and animals that arrived on the islands became adapted to new conditions.

The object of this book is to give an account of the animal life of the Galapagos Islands, and one of the most difficult problems has been to decide what to leave out. In general most reptiles and birds have been described and many illustrated, but with marine life it was impossible to deal with the myriad of species that throng the shallow waters. Representative species were chosen which the visitor might be likely to come across, otherwise the task of description would be of gigantic proportions and quite outside the scope of this book.

Another difficulty is that, in the case of many groups of animals, little organized collecting and study have been undertaken so that what is known about the presence of many species is scattered amongst obscure scientific journals.

The two sets of island names caused a number of problems concerning the policy that should be adopted in this book. It is true that a growing number of persons, associated in one way or another with the Galapagos, have learned to use the official Spanish-language Ecuadorian names. On the other hand, an even greater number of visitors, scientific and otherwise, find the original English names slip off the tongue far more easily and these are the names used by Herman Melville. It was decided, therefore, that, in the text, the English language names would be used. In the numbered list, however, the numbering is that given by Thornton, together with the official Ecuadorian names and their associated English names.

CHAPTER 1

History of the Archipelago

There are no indigenous peoples of the Galapagos. In pre-recorded times, if human beings arrived at these islands then they left without leaving evidence of their visit. The first document giving irrefutable evidence of a visitor putting his foot on Galapagean territory was a letter written by a bishop of Panama in 1535. On a voyage from Panama to Peru, his ship became becalmed, then drifted in the Humboldt Current at the Equator, directly westwards, where he came across the Galapagos. This was Fray Tomás de Berlanga, and it is his letter to Emperor Carlos V of Spain that gives the first account of giant tortoises, iguanas and the extremely tame birds. The bishop was without water and his crew found so little that they had to chew cactus pads.

However, some credence has been given to a story that a fifteenth-century Inca king, Tupac Yuapangui, heard that there were uninhabited islands in the seas to the west. Setting sail from Guayaquil, he went to see for himself. He was away for between nine months and a year and found two islands: Nina-Chumbi, meaning Island of Fire, and Hahua-Chumbi, meaning the Outer Island. Island of Fire could well have signified an active volcano. It is possible, therefore, that these could have been islands of the Galapagos. The sundry items he brought back with him, however, could not possibly have been obtained from the Galapagos. These were: black peoples, silver and gold, a brass chair and the skin and jawbone of a horse! If, indeed, he did get to the Galapagos, he also visited other places on the South American coast and could have made an extensive voyage in the time he was away.

The first visitor to the Galapagos after Bishop Tomás was Diego de Rivadeneira who, with eleven other Spaniards, also found himself, unwillingly, in the Archipelago due to current and wind, against which they could not bring their 'stolen' ship to sail. He was twenty-five days in the Pacific and drifting along the Equator. Water, of course, was what he was most in need of and he did not find any. However, he left an account of this adventure in which the tortoises, iguanas and the Galapagos Hawk are referred to, as well as the extreme tameness of all the creatures. Diego de Rivadeneira did not put a name to the islands, but the volcanoes and the animals leave no doubt as to his Galapagos visit.

Bishop Tomás and Diego de Rivadeneira were quickly followed to the Galapagos by a number of Spanish navigators who christened the islands Islas Encantadas or Bewitched Islands. But other names were given too, including Las Huérfanas or The Orphans, and, rather more significantly, Insulae de los Galopegos or Islands of the Tortoises.

In the meantime, the various islands of the Archipelago had a variety of names bestowed on them to which we shall refer later. However, in 1892, the Government of Ecuador, who had claimed the islands, gave an official name to the group to mark the 400th anniversary of the discovery of America by Columbus. In spite of the virtually overwhelming use of Galapagos as a name for the island group, the official name given to it was Archipiélago de Colon, or The Islands of Columbus. The first chart to show the Galapagos is dated 1570.

Towards the end of the seventeenth century the coasts of Central America were ravaged by pirates and buccaneers. The latter had their origin in labour recruited for the slaughtering of feral cattle in Haiti, in which island they abounded. The meat was smoked over large fires called *boucans* and those who tended the smoking operation were called *boucannières*. These gangs were a lawless lot and were used often for military repression in the violent politics of the Caribbean. They found themselves so strong that they formed private bands for harassing the Spanish. Although the buccaneers were murderous ruffians, they included amongst their number some remarkable men. Several were first-class navigators and mapmakers— indeed their maps were exceptionally accurate compared with the contemporary Spanish ones. Perhaps the most outstanding buccaneer was William Dampier (1652–1715). Several bands of buccaneers established themselves on the Pacific coast and central and northern South America and preyed upon the Spanish ships taking treasure southwards.

Many buccaneering bands made the Galapagos their headquarters because, although sitting astride the trade route, they were yet far enough away to discourage pursuit. Here they could rest up and supply their ships with water and tortoise meat. Dampier was a regular visitor to the Galapagos. James Bay, on James Island, was much frequented by these lawless bands and evidence of their having been there can still be seen.

The whaling era commenced about 1780 when both British and American vessels took part in what must have been a gigantic exploitation of the teeming Humboldt Current. During the eighty or so years which followed, the whalers and sealers brought about significant changes in the fauna of the Galapagos. Not only were large numbers of several species of whales taken, to the extent that the numbers have never recovered, but tens of thousands of fur seals were killed also. Vessels usually remained on the whaling grounds for two years or more and during this time, and the long voyage home round Cape Horn, tortoise meat was eaten. On reaching the Galapagos, landing parties would go ashore to search for Giant Tortoises. They were taken aboard and stacked like barrels, remaining alive without water or food for over a year unti they were slaughtered to provide fresh meat and oil. Both of these commodities were of the highest quality, the oil replacing butter.

The Post Office barrel on Charles was placed in position by a British whaler some time before 1793. Ships arriving would deposit mail in the barrel and it would be picked up by vessels homeward bound. The original barrel is no longer there, but a new 'barrel' operates the same procedure. Unfortunately, almost every ship that has paid a visit to it has left its name on driftwood and similar surfaces so that it has the appearance of a junk yard. Nevertheless it possesses some romance especially to the philatelist.

It is not known precisely at what date the various domestic animals (which have since turned feral) reached the islands, but ships' cats would certainly have had an opportunity of getting ashore during the 1780–1800 period.

Patrick Watkins, an Irishman, was the first known permanent resident of the Galapagos. He was put ashore, willingly or unwillingly, on Charles in 1807 and he stayed for two years. He was able to grow vegetables, some of which he traded for rum, and various accounts state that he was always intoxicated. He kept several men in a system of slavery and ultimately escaped from the island by stealing a boat from a whaler whilst its crew were ashore looking for water and tortoises. He took five slaves with him, but only he reached Guayaquil.

In 1832 Ecuador formally took possession of the Galapagos Islands after General José Villamil had strongly urged this course. Following an early colonization attempt on Charles, a penal settlement was established.

The arrival of HMS *Beagle* at the Galapagos, on 16 September 1835, set an entirely new pattern in types of visitors. This was a surveying ship of the Royal Navy under the command of Captain Fitzroy, RN, and a naturalist, Charles Darwin, aged twenty-six, was on board. On anchoring they had already spent three years at sea and the voyage was to last almost another two years before reaching England. Chatham, Charles, Albemarle and James Islands were visited. The animal life of these islands, set against the geological background, had a profound effect on the young Darwin. He was a good geologist and his reasoning powers were acute, and the voyage, which Captain Fitzroy hoped would put an end to any speculation that the animals and plants of the world had been fashioned by any other means than creation by God, had a very different end. Darwin was to spend the voyage merely amusing himself, passing the time until he had matured enough to become a country parson. However his deductive reasoning put an end to that. He quarrelled bitterly with Fitzroy who later committed suicide.

The visit of Darwin was one of the most momentous happenings in the development of human thought. A number of men had tried to put into words their profound disbelief in the Creation. Indeed, Charles Darwin's grandfather was one! But the world, at least the Christian world, needed some positive proof that life had evolved from simpler forms and this proof needed to be strong enough to confront the religious bigotry of the time. Charles Darwin realized that he had come across such proof in the Galapagos and his subsequent writings, although causing fierce argument and controversy, were finally accepted as the broad basis of a theory of evolution.

Many scientific expeditions and individual collectors followed in the wake of the *Beagle* to collect specimens of plants and animals. These were taken from many different islands in order to observe the degree of variation that occurred among the many isolated populations.

Seventeen years after the *Beagle*'s voyage, the royal Swedish frigate *Eugenie*, under the command of C. A. Virgin, visited Chatham, Indefatigable, Charles, James and Albemarle islands on a voyage around the world. The visit was of eleven days only. Twenty-one years then passed before the Agassiz expedition visited Charles, Albemarle, James, Jervis and Indefatigable islands. This visit only lasted ten days and was carried out by the steamer *Hassler*.

The second British ship was HMS *Herald* captained by Sir Henry Kellett, CB, accompanied by HMS *Pandora* commanded by Lt Wood. The visit was for ten days only in 1846.

Another British ship to make a scientific collection was HMS *Peterel*, under Commander W. E. Cookson. This was in June 1878, and Abingdon, Charles and Albemarle islands were visited. Following this there were two visits by the *Albatross* of the US Fish Commission, firstly in 1888, when L. A. Lee and C. H. Townsend made collections, and, secondly, in 1891 when Alexander Agassiz made a five-day collecting tour.

After the US Fish Commission's visits there followed a long period of interest by several United States scientific bodies and universities, as well as by private persons wealthy enough to charter an ocean-going ship. The Hopkins Stanford Galapagos Expedition of 1898–9 stayed six months, while R. E. Snodgrass and E. Heller got together a large collection, later unfortunately mostly destroyed. This was the start of the great interest in the natural history of the Galapagos taken by the Washington Academy of Science. The California Academy of Science Expedition lasted exactly a year, from September 1905, and the entomologist F. X. Williams made large insect collections. Seventeen years then elapsed before the next important visit. This was by the *Harrison Williams* and the well known naturalists William Beebe and William Morton Wheeler. Although the yacht *Noma* sailed around for twenty-one days, only 100 hours were spent on land. Beebe produced his important well illustrated book *Galapagos, World's End*.

It was not until nearly fifty years after the visit of the *Peterel* that the next British expedition collected in the islands, in 1924. This was the *St George* Expedition on the steam yacht of the name, and the collectors were three entomologists of repute, C. L. Collenette and the Misses C. Longfield and E. Cheesman. A large collection of insects was made and it has been a great privilege to examine and draw some of the specimens.

The following year William Beebe was again collecting, this time from the *Arcturus*, but stayed less than a month. In the same year, however, the Norwegian Zoological Expedition stayed five months, visiting Floreana, Chatham and Santa Cruz. The Field Museum of Natural History at Chicago came in next and stayed ten days during the Cornelius Crane Pacific Expedition. This was the visit of the brigantine yacht *Illyria* in 1929. The Gifford Pinchot Expedition stayed for five weeks during the same year. This was in the yacht *Mary Pinchot* and their collections are deposited in the US National Museum. The following year saw the Vincent Astor Expedition to the Galapagos on the *Nourmahal*. They stayed fifteen days.

The Hancock Galapagos Expedition on the R/V *Velero III* visited most islands at various dates from December 1931 to January 1938, and during this time the Templeton Crocker Expedition of the Californian Academy of Sciences, on the schooner *Zaia*, visited most islands. During the same period, too, the Darwin Memorial Expedition, with Wolfgang von Hagen, collecting especially the termites, visited from September 1935 to February 1936 (Darwin's centennial anniversary). This produced two well known general accounts *Ecuador the Unknown* (1940) and *Two and a half years' travels in the Republic of Ecuador and the Galapagos Islands* (1949).

Coming now to more modern times, the Hans Haas Expedition with Irenäus Eibl-Eibesfeldt as biologist, made a visit from November 1953 to January 1954 on the yacht *Xarifa*. This resulted in the general book *Galapagos—Noah's Ark of the Pacific*. The last visit of scientists we shall mention was the Deutsche Galapagos Expedition which arrived at the end of 1962 with Eberland Curio as biologist.

Naming the islands

The first chart to show individual names for the separate islands appeared in 1684, was prepared by Ambrose Cowley, and it was over a hundred years before Captain Colnett issued his charts in 1793 and 1794. Today any visitor to the Galapagos cannot but be confused at the multiplicity of names. Each island has at least two names and not until one has learnt them all, by constant reference to a map showing all the names, can one appreciate the location of any author whose writing is being studied. Each island has an English name and many have Spanish names—in fact, several bear two Spanish names! In 1892 Ecuador issued an official list of names, but whilst the larger islands have official Spanish names, many of the smaller islands have retained their English ones.

There is another complication in the use of the names of individual islands. This is that a number of modern writers who give lists of the islands also indicate their own 'preferred usage' names. Thus, the names dodge about from English and Spanish to 'official' in the course of a single narrative.

Galapagos Islands (Archipielago de Colon)

	English name	Official name	Other names
1	Culpepper	Darwin	Guerra
2	Wenman	Wolf	Nunez, Gasna, Genovesa, Ewres
3	Narborough	Fernandina	Plata
4	Albemarle	Isabela	Santa Gertrudis
5	Abingdon	Pinta	Gerandino
6	Bindloe	Marchena	Torres
7	Tower	Genovesa	Ewres
8	James	San Salvador	Santiago, Olmedo, Gil, York
9	Jervis	Rábida	
10	Duncan	Pinzón	Dean
11	North Seymour	Seymour	
12	South Seymour	Baltra	
13	Indefatigable	Santa Cruz	Bolivia, Norfolk, Porter, Valdez
14	Plaza Islets	Plaza	
15	Barrington	Santa Fé	
16	Charles	Santa María	Floreana
17	Chatham	San Cristóbal	Dassigney, Grande
18	Hood	Española	

The new visitors

Within the last few years a new type of visitor is arriving on the islands in ever-increasing numbers—the tourist. Unfortunately the word 'tourist' in the minds of many people has rather a disagreeable connotation. It oftens conjures up an image of brashness and of people ill-informed and ill-equipped, spending too little time observing what they have spent a great deal of money to come and see. Actually this is not the true picture of the Galapagos tourists. In the first place, the Galapagos, being one of the last wild places to come within the reach of modern transport, would not appeal to those who like to spend the whole day lying in the sun and the night at sophisticated nightclubs. There is no place in the Galapagos for such a tourist and it is earnestly hoped that the authorities will lend no encouragement to those who might seek to gain from altering the present situation.

It has been suggested that tourism will increase dramatically within the next decade, and that, as a result of this, the dangers of pollution and the degradation of the environment will become worse, causing the pressures on the wildlife and its general habitat to become greater. This is undoubtedly true, but armed with the knowledge that the dangers (associated with human pressure) are present, externally from tourism and internally from the Galapagos inhabitants, would it not be the wisest possible move to plan to counter such factors of habitat degradation at the earliest possible moment? It is no wish of the writer to persuade, induce, or stimulate his readers to collect specimens in the Galapagos, nor even to do so much as to turn over a stone to look for beetles or geckos. Many of the creatures mentioned in this book may go unobserved by the visitor for this reason. In Academy Bay on Sta. Cruz Island, the Charles Darwin Research Station is developing, in conjunction with the Ecuadorian National Park Service, a visitors' information centre. All visitors are encouraged to visit the centre which will help them to a greater appreciation of the islands, their flora and fauna, and their history; they will also more fully appreciate the need to protect and preserve the islands and their natural inhabitants.

CHAPTER 2

Land Mammals

Native land mammals are poorly represented in the Galapagos. The sea is a formidable barrier to land-mammal dispersal. Only eight species occur in the Archipelago and these consist of six endemic rice rats of the genus *Oryzomys* and two bats of the genus *Lasiurus*, one of which is endemic.

RICE RATS, *Oryzomys* spp

This genus of rodents, the members of which are called Rice Rats, is confined to North and South America. Only one species, however, *O. palustris*, is found in North America where it is distributed widely in about eighteen of the south-eastern states. Many species of the genus are to be found in Central and South America. *Oryzomys* rats have blunt heads with medium-sized ears similar in proportion to those of the North American wood rats, *Neotoma* spp. The tail is long and scaly—usually as long as the body or somewhat longer. The skull bears 16 teeth, and there are 8 mammae. Little is known of the biology of the Galapagos species, but it is likely that they feed on green vegetation and seeds, and are nocturnal. They make surface runways and nest under debris. They breed throughout the year and usually 3–4 young are born; 3–4 litters being produced annually. The young are born blind and almost naked, and are sexually mature at about 50 days. Rice rats are so called because in those areas where rice is grown they are associated with damage which is sometimes considerable.

The six Galapagos species of *Oryzomys* are as follows:

O. swarthi, James
O. galapagoensis, Chatham

O. narboroughi, Narborough
O. indefessus, Indefatigable
O. darwini, Indefatigable
O. bauri, Barrington

BATS, *Lasiurus* spp

Two species of bats are recorded, *Lasiurus brachyotis* and *L. cinereus*. The genus is well distributed on the American mainland and the latter species is known as the Hoary Bat in North America. This is on account of the yellowish-brown to mahogany-brown fur, the individual hairs of which are tipped with white. Generally members of this genus are found in wooded areas and roost in trees. They are well known migrants, those found in North America moving southwards in autumn.

CAT, *Felis felis*

As to whether the Black Rat or domestic cat was the first predator introduced by man to the Archipelago is open to doubt, but the cat has played an important part in reducing the number of several endemic species in those islands where it has run wild. It feeds on the young of reptiles (iguanas and tortoises) and birds. So many of the latter are ground-nesters, that innumerable opportunities for predation are presented. Cats occur in several types of locality: they search the coastal strip, obviously for cast-up dead fish and crustacea, etc, and they are to be found around the rim of high volcanoes.

Cats occur on Charles, Indefatigable, Albemarle, Chatham and possibly on James. They breed in holes and cavities in the lava.

BLACK RAT, *Rattus rattus*

The Black Rat and the Brown Rat, *Rattus norvegicus*, are probably the two most important mammalian pests of man. The former is common in many areas of the Galapagos, but the latter is absent. Both species harbour the Rat Flea, *Xenopsylla cheopis*, which in turn transmits pathogenic organisms responsible for bubonic plague. The urine of both rats also carries the organisms causing the often-lethal Weil's disease.

The Black Rat exists in two colour-phases, black and brown, so that colour is of secondary importance in identification if the observed animal is brown. The best distinguishing feature of the two *Rattus* species is the length of the tail. In the Brown Rat the tail is shorter than the head and body length, whereas in the Black Rat the tail is longer. The Black Rat is chiefly found around sea ports, and usually occupies the upper stories of buildings. It does not require soil in which to burrow as does the Brown Rat.

The Black Rat occurs on James, Albemarle, Duncan, Chatham and Charles, but does not occur on the uninhabited Culpepper, Wenman, Abingdon, Bindloe, Tower, Hood, Barrington and Narborough. On the former group the Black Rat has been credited with the large reduction in numbers of the native rats.

HOUSE MOUSE, Mus musculus

Originating in the Old World, the House Mouse is now found almost throughout the world wherever people are concentrated. Although usually associated with buildings, where they will feed on almost anything edible, in tropical areas they often infest growing crops. This mouse is greyish-brown with a grey or buff belly, and the length of head and body varies from 80–85 mm (3–3.5 in), and the tail from 70–95 mm (2.5–3.5 in). The fur is short and the tail is scaly. This is a very prolific species and when conditions are favourable, with abundant food, the population soon builds up to pest proportions. It commences to breed at 6 weeks, with litters from 3–11 in number. The gestation period is 18–21 days and there are several litters a year.

DOMESTIC CATTLE, Bos taurus

Domestic cattle live in a feral or semi-feral condition on those islands where there have been human settlements. Introduced cattle without adequate fencing soon became adapted to looking after themselves in free range.

The feral cattle of southern Albemarle date from soon after 1909 when they ranged on the higher altitudes of the volcano Sierra Negra. These were cropped by the inhabitants of the small village of Santo Tomas which had been established at about 600 m (2,000 ft) by Don Antonio Gil of Guayaquil. The cattle are preyed upon by packs of wild dog which attack the calves. Wild cattle are also present on Charles and Indefatigable, although on the latter island they are much less abundant than formerly. It was reported to me by one of the present Norwegian settlers that whereas a few years ago he could go out to hunt wild cattle with a reasonable chance of success, today he would be more likely to return empty-handed.

His own considerable domestic herd, now maintained in lush, well fenced meadows, was originally established by corralling feral animals. An unusual feature of a proportion of the present herd is the heavy, warty growths with which the animals are covered.

FERAL PIG, Sus scrofa

Domestic pigs introduced by settlers have run wild with consequent serious harm to the indigenous animals and plants. It is believed that on James they have exterminated the Land Iguanas which were so abundant at the time of Darwin's visit. They have materially assisted in the dispersal of the seeds of the introduced guava which, in turn, has depressed the populations of the endemic plants. They have also destroyed the nests of tortoises, eating both young and hatchlings before they have grown sufficiently to resist their omnivorous attack. Ground-nesting birds, as well as those which inhabit burrows, are seriously affected, not only by disturbance, but also by being caught on the nest and consumed. Feral pigs were already on Charles when visited by Darwin in 1835, and are now present on all the islands where there have been settlements. A recent photograph of Galapagos Hawks around goat carcases shows a bristly, light-coloured boar with black spots and strong tusks.

DONKEY, Equus asinus

Donkeys are used as pack animals. Many have been able to escape from domesticity and now live as feral animals. On the slopes of Volcan Alcedo, on Albemarle, donkeys are particularly abundant, but as the Giant Tortoise is also common in the same locality it is not thought that the donkey causes much harm to their environment. Donkeys occur on James, Albemarle, Chatham, Indefatigable and Charles.

FERAL DOG, Canis canis

The feral or wild dogs of the Galapagos are fierce predators. They roam in small packs and will attack man, as Dr Thornton relates. They occur on Chatham, Indefatigable, Charles and Albemarle, all islands where human settlements occur. They feed on reptiles, young birds, kids and calves, and have played an important part in reducing the numbers of tortoises and other endemic species. There are very few accounts of their appearance, but Beebe described them as like police dogs—presumably this would imply the

Alsatian breed—but he goes on to say that they had some white on them. It is said that dogs have eliminated the goats on Charles.

GOAT, *Capra hircus*

Goats must have been introduced to the Galapagos by the buccaneers, as the first recorded attempt to control them was in 1700 when dogs were released for the purpose. However, goats were purposely introduced to the various islands on a number of occasions. They are known to have been released on James in 1814, and again in 1906, and even as recently as 1957 fishermen released some on Abingdon as a source of fresh meat. All the islands where there are settlements support substantial numbers of wild goats. In addition they occur on uninhabited James, Abingdon and Bindloe. The Ecuadorian National Park Service has recently succeeded in exterminating them from both Barrington and Hood and have greatly reduced the numbers on both Abingdon and Bindloe. On some islands they are numbered in thousands, and, because of their destruction of the vegetative cover, denying it to the endemic animals, they are considered to be the most undesirable of the feral species. Their destruction is considered to be one of the most important components of conservation in the Galapagos. Thornton describes them as handsome creatures coloured uniformly black or brown, the males having magnificent spiralling and spreading horns.

CHAPTER 3

Sea Lions and Seals

The sea lions, seals and walruses constitute the suborder PINNIPEDIA of the CARNIVORA. They differ from the CARNIVORA VERA or FISSIPEDIA in showing special modifications which adapt them for an aquatic or, more especially, a marine mode of life. (A few seals are to be found in fresh-water lakes.) The body is streamlined and the fore and hind limbs are modified to give them a fin-like appearance. The limb segments nearest the body are short, whereas the distal ones are elongated and all the digits are webbed. The dentition is of interest in that the incisor teeth are reduced in numbers whilst the carnassials, the large grinding teeth characteristic of the FISSIPEDIA, are absent. There is a tendency for the nails of the digits to be small, but those of the first and fifth digit of the hind feet are larger than the others. It is also of interest that in the brain the cerebral hemispheres are exceptionally convoluted.

Only one of the three families in the PINNIPEDIA is represented in the Galapagos. This is the OTARIIDAE, or eared seal in which both the Galapagos Sea Lion and the Galapagos Fur Seal are included.

GALAPAGOS SEA LION, Zalophus californianus wollebackii

The Galapagos Sea Lion is a subspecies of the well known Californian Sea Lion and is endemic to the Galapagos. Although this is one of the smaller species, the males are disproportionately large, often being several times the weight of their cows. The adult males are also characterized by a high, bulging forehead, the skull show a high sagital crest. Both sexes are dark chocolate-brown in colour although there appears to be some variation, some females being almost creamy. It is common throughout the Galapagos and breeding colonies occur on many islands where there are sandy beaches,

28

The bull Sea Lion, *Zalophus californianus wollebackii*

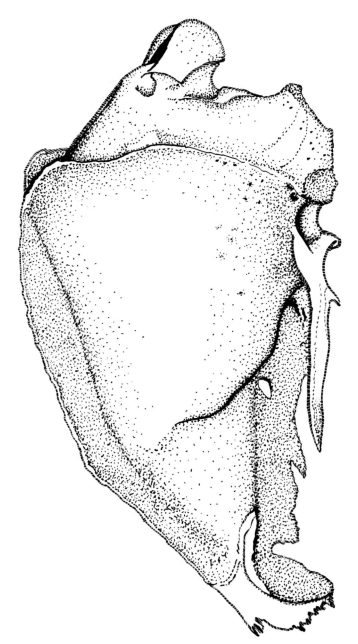

Skull of the male Galapagos Sea Lion

The cow Sea Lion, *Zalophus californianus wollebackii*

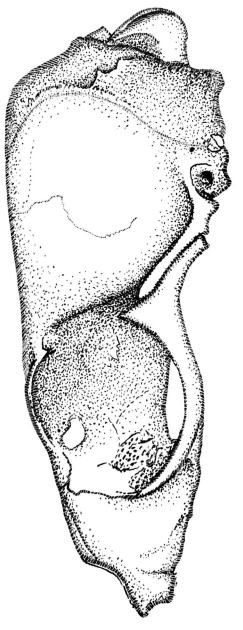

Skull of the female Galapagos Sea Lion

or where flat rocks can be negotiated. Even though ungainly, they are able to make their way fairly quickly over very rugged rocky areas and often travel considerable distances from the shore to find shade.

The bull collects a harem of about half a dozen cows, but sometimes as many as thirty. He guards them jealously and is constantly on patrol, ready to chase away intruders. They recognize each other by smelling noses, and when the bull returns to the beach after a spell in the water he visits each cow for recognition. The bulls often fight and many are heavily scarred.

A single pup is born and then suckled for two years. It has a comparatively large head whilst the skin is loose and folded. The continuous noise on the sea lion beach is due to the barking of the bull as he swims up and down opposite his piece of beach, and the plaintive bleating of pups trying to find their mothers. Sea lion cows turn savagely on strange pups attempting to suckle. They are, however, playful in the water when humans swim amongst them.

Sea lions are characterized by the presence of their relatively prominent ears, small number of underfur hairs, and on the hind flippers the outer digits are longer than the three inner ones. In addition, the hind flippers are separated from each other and the tail, enabling them to progress on land with greater facility than true seals.

The female Galapagos Sea Lions are exceptionally tame and will usually allow a person to walk within a metre or so. Occasionally one, probably one about to give birth, will rear up and snarl. The young ones are also very tame and it is delightful to watch a small group of four or five rolling and playing about together in the tidal pools. The master bull, however, has to be watched, as he is continuously on the move, either swimming up and down along his piece of beach on which his cows are lying, or lunging ashore to see them and touch noses. The human intruder must not be caught unawares as the bull will hurl himself up the beach at a surprising speed for such a large, ungainly animal on land.

GALAPAGOS FUR SEAL, Arctocephalus australis galapagoensis.

This second member of the eared seals, OTARIIDAE, is placed in the subfamily ARCTOCEPHALINAE, the so-called fur seals. The Galapagos Sea Lion originated from the north, the south. The fur seal appears to be much less heat-tolerant than the sea lion. Instead of

The Galapagos Fur Seal, *Arctocephalus australis galapagoensis*

lying out on the beaches in the full sun, the fur seal spends much time in caves and grottoes and, indeed, is confined to rocky areas where deep shade can be found.

The fur seal is small, with the head much broader and the snout much less pronounced than in the sea lion. The generic name, *Arctocephalus*, signifies bear head, which is very descriptive. The fur consists of a dense undercoat of short hair and an outer layer of abundant guard hairs. This gives the rusty cinnamon-brown coat a bristly appearance when dry. The eyes are large and look sad and gentle. Whereas the sea lion barks, the fur seal lows like a cow. In the past the fur seal has suffered much from man, and their numbers dwindled—however, as a result of strict conservation regulations introduced by the Ecuadorian authorities, their numbers have increased remarkably, the first-ever comprehensive survey, conducted in early 1979, revealed a total population of between 30,000 and 40,000.

CHAPTER 4

Whales and Dolphins

The novice observer, cruising or sailing in fauna-rich waters, should be able to differentiate between a shark, a whale and a dolphin as his first lesson. Often a sighting is only of a second or so's duration so that the following differences must be committed to memory.

In the first place, whales and dolphins are air-breathing and so must come to the surface from time to time when the air, which has been through the lungs, is exhaled—sometimes with considerable force—and fresh air taken in through the blowhole situated at the top of the head. Sharks on the other hand, are fish and take in water through the mouth and pass it out through the rows of parallel gill-slits at the side of the head. They do not, therefore, have to come to the surface in order to 'breathe'. The second important point is that the tail-fins, or flukes, of a whale or dolphin are horizontal, whereas the tail-fin of a shark is vertical. This fin is often large in size so that, when swimming near the surface, the back-fin and the upper tail-fin are both frequently out of the water.

Whales

Although whales are such large animals they are often difficult to identify at sea. Positive identifications are usually made from stranded specimens or when one has been killed and brought onto the deck of a whaling ship.

The Galapagos Islands were the headquarters of a considerable whaling industry for many years, but today the numbers have been so reduced that their hunting is no longer economically viable. They may now be increasing in numbers from the very low level to which they once fell.

The CETACEA, that is the whales, dolphins and porpoises, are mammals, with warm blood, and they breathe air. The young develops within the body of the mother for a number of months as a foetus, and when born is suckled until it is able to obtain its own food. Mammals are characterized by being clothed with hair, but the CETACEA, being highly modified for their marine existence, have lost practically all their hairy covering. In young animals, however, a trace of hair is usually to be found on the snout and chin. Spending all their existence in water with no opportunity for being warmed by the sun's heat, they are insulated from loss of body heat by a thick layer of fat known as blubber.

During the evolution of the whale, fitting it for its mode of existence, the forelimbs have been modified into flippers but, although fin-like, their bone structure is comparable with that of a land mammal. The hindlimbs have been lost externally, but their bony rudiments may be found within the body. The horizontally flattened tail, or flukes, do not possess a bony skeleton, but are composed of skin and fibrous tissue. The nostrils are known as blowholes which may be single or double and they open on the top of the head towards the back.

CETACEA are classified into two main groups, the whalebone whales and the toothed whales. The whalebone whales do not possess teeth but, across the mouth cavity, hang a number of triangular plates which are heavily fringed, called baleen. The whales swim along, taking in planktonic organisms which are caught on the baleen and then swallowed.

Of the whalebone whales, two species not uncommonly sighted in Galapagean waters are the Common Rorqual, *Balaenoptera physalis* and the Sei Whale, *Balaenoptera borealis*.

COMMON RORQUAL, *Balaenoptera physalis*

This whale is generally about 21 m (70 ft) in length, but may reach as much as another 3 m (10 ft). It is found throughout the great oceans and makes extensive migrations. The back is greyish, whilst the belly is white. There is, however, an unusual asymmetry with regard to the coloration of the head, in that the right of the lower jaw is white and the left is grey. There are a number of parallel grooves on the throat and chest and the back-fin, which is situated on the back third of the body, is fairly high and roughly triangular, with the hinder edge concave.

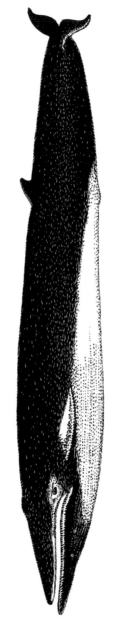

The Common Rorqual, *Balaenoptera physalis*

The Sei Whale, *Balaenoptera borealis*

The general shape of the body is long and slender. The snout is broad and low with its margins forming an acute angle, whereas in the Blue Whale they are nearly parallel for most of their length.

SEI WHALE, *Balaenoptera borealis*

This whale, of worldwide distribution, is slightly smaller than the Common Rorqual, usually about 15 m (50 ft) in length, although it may reach another 3 m (10 ft). It is rather less slender than the Common Rorqual but has that species' low and acutely pointed snout. The back-fin is relatively larger than that of the Blue Whale or Common Rorqual, and the apex points backwards. The concave hinder margin is very pronounced. The pigmentation is symmetrical and is bluish-grey on the back, whilst the belly is somewhat lighter. Parallel grooves on the throat and chest are present and there is a whitish area on the throat not extending as far forward as the chin.

SPERM WHALE, *Physeter catodon*

Otherwise called the Cachalot, *Physeter catodon* is the largest of the toothed whales. Males attain a length of 18 m (60 ft), whilst females reach only half this length. The head is of extraordinary size and almost square when viewed from the side. The colour is dark bluish-grey, light grey on the under-surface and almost white on the lower side of front head and lower jaw. The back-fin is represented only as a hump and a few smaller humps occur between it and the tail-flukes. The large teeth, which may be as much as 20 cm (8 in) in length, are present in the lower jaw only and fit into sockets in the upper jaw.

It is normally found in tropical waters.

KILLER WHALE, *Orcinus orca*

The Killer, or Grampus, is a widely distributed toothed whale of ferocious habit. It preys on seals, sea lions, other whales, penguins and other large animals it happens to encounter. Hunting in small packs, it may be found in Antarctic, Arctic and tropical waters. It is often seen in Galapagos waters and is stated to have overturned sailing boats around the area. It may be easily distinguished from other small whale and dolphin species by the contrasting black-and-white coloration, and by the large upwardly-pointing and long back-fin. In addition, there is a white patch behind the eye, a crescent-

The Sperm Whale, *Physeter catodon*

The Killer Whale, *Orcinus orca*

shaped patch immediately behind the back-fin, and a white lobe on the side between the back-fin and the flukes. Males grow up to 9 m (30 ft) in length and the back-fin may be as much as 1·5 m (6 ft) in length. The tail-flukes are also very large. Females reach a length of 4·5 m (15 ft).

Dolphins

Two species of dolphin are found in Galapagos waters so commonly that they are almost certain to be seen by anyone cruising around the islands. These are the Common Dolphin, *Delphinus delphis*, and the Bottle-nosed Dolphin, *Tursiops truncatus*. No doubt other species make their way from time to time through these rich feeding areas.

BOTTLE-NOSED DOLPHIN, *Tursiops truncatus*

This is the species of dolphin most likely to be seen 'piloting' or swimming in front of ships in Galapagos waters. A couple, or up to a dozen or more, swim within a metre or so of the prow, crossing over from side to side and staying for half an hour or so. They can often be seen swimming towards the ship from considerable distances. As their eyes are only momentarily out of the water they must hear or use some pressure-wave perception in order to locate the object to which they are attracted A great point of interest, which can be observed when they are swimming close to the prow, is the quite remarkable co-ordination existing between the mother and the young. However the mother twists and turns, the young follows as though fixed to the mother's side, seemingly within a few centimetres.

The Bottle-nosed Dolphin has an upper surface very dark in colour, including both sides of the flippers and flukes. Behind the vent, the lower surface is similarly coloured, but elsewhere, on the belly and throat, it is white. In size it grows up to about 4 m (12 ft). The snout or beak is prominent but only about 7·5 cm (3 in) in length. There are 22–25 teeth on each side of the upper and lower jaws.

COMMON DOLPHIN, *Delphinus delphis*

The Common Dolphin is much less robust in general appearance than the Bottle-nosed. It is more slender and 'stream-lined' and also

The Bottle-nosed Dolphin, *Tursiops truncatus*

The Common Dolphin, *Delphinus delphis*

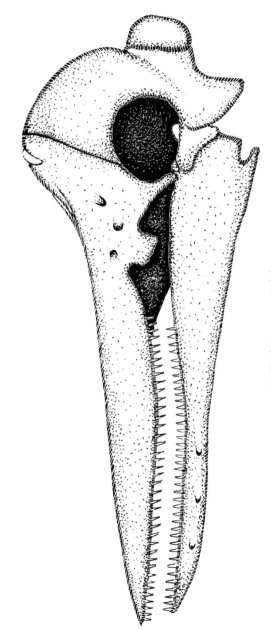

Skull of Common Dolphin

smaller, seldom exceeding 2·5 m (8 ft) in total length, more usually about 1·5 m (6 ft). The dark pigmentation of the back does not reach far down the sides except in the region of the back-fin. The well defined snout or beak is narrow and about 15 cm (6 in) in length. Circling the eye is a black mark which then extends forwards around the base of the beak. Two dark streaks extend along the side, the upper one joined to the pigmented area in the region of the back-fin. Another dark streak extends from the base of the flippers along the sides of the lower jaw. The hinder end of the body is slender when compared with Bottle-nosed Dolphin. There are 40–50 teeth on each side of the upper and lower jaws.

The Common Dolphin often occurs in large schools—upwards of 200 is not uncommon—but is not so attracted to swimming along with ships. A great sight is to see a school moving across the sea at speed and hurling themselves into the air at intervals so that there may be dozens airborne at the same time.

CHAPTER 5

Land Birds

GALAPAGOS FLAMINGO, Phoenicopterus ruber ssp

Flamingoes, which are amongst the most beautiful birds in the world have given difficulty concerning their classification. At one time they were thought to be closely related to ducks and geese and were classified close to gallinaceous birds. Nowadays they are grouped with storks and ibises. They are easy to identify. Their necks and legs, which are longer in proportion to the body than any other birds, and their curiously bent beaks make them exceedingly easy to pick out, even at a great distance. They are white with varying amounts of pink or red, with the wing-tips and the end of the beak black. In flight their necks are stretched out forwards whilst their legs trail behind and they appear to 'talk' to each other in the manner of geese.

There are only four species in the world, although there are a number of subspecies. The Galapagos Flamingo, of which there are only about 500 in the whole of the Archipelago, is a subspecies of the Greater Flamingo, *Phoenicopterus ruber*. Of the many subspecies, it is the most vivid in colour and strongly reminiscent of the Scarlet Ibis (*Eudocimus ruber*).

All flamingoes are found in sheltered lagoons or shallow brackish or saltish fresh water, where the nutrient-rich water abounds with organisms. The flamingo walks in a stately manner through the water, bending its head down from time to time and moving its beak from front to back. In this way the bottom mandible of the beak is uppermost and the small organisms are sieved out.

It is inevitable that such a showy bird of gorgeous plumage should be much disturbed and this is certainly true of our Galapagos birds. They must be approached with extreme caution, keeping out of

American Flamingo, *Phoenicopterus ruber*

sight behind shrubs, and at the same time maintaining the utmost silence. Only then will their dignified stroll through the shallows be observed—one of the great natural sights of the Galapagos, thrilling whoever gains the privilege of this extraordinary avian observation.

GALAPAGOS HAWK, *Buteo galapagoensis*

Two hundred pairs only are thought to be the total population of this species and, therefore, this must be one of the rarest birds in the world. Although somewhat similar to Swainson's Hawk, *Buteo swainsoni*, of western North America and the Zone-tailed Hawk, *Buteo albonotatus*, of Central America and northern South America, it is a distinct species found only in the Galapagos. It is extremely tame, allowing of a very close approach, and this must have contributed to a decrease in numbers as it was formerly much more abundant.

The genus *Buteo* is an extensive one, there being no fewer than twenty-six species. In Britain these are known as buzzards and have been so-called for four centuries. British observers will see the great similarity of the Galapagos Hawk to the Common Buzzard, *B. buteo*, of Britain. The main difference being the fresher, rather more vivid, colouring in the former species.

The Galapagos Hawk is easy to identify as it is the only member of the FALCONIFORMES or hawks likely to be encountered in the Galapagos. Two species, however—the Osprey, *Pandion haliaetus*, and the Peregrine, *Falco peregrinus*—occasionally visit the Galapagos as migrants. But the buzzard with the yellow feet and legs and barred tail is the Galapagos Hawk. It can often be seen soaring and wheeling high in the sky whilst it searches the ground for small prey, such as young iguanas, rats, lizards, centipedes and carrion. It has been seen by the writer to hover for some minutes at the top of a gulley at the side of a cliff (Hood Island) and from that position make several unsuccessful strikes at a mocking bird, returning each time to its hovering position. Indeed, in addition to the prey detailed above, it will drop on a number of bird species.

It constructs a large nest of sticks on shrubs or trees, and sometimes right out in the open on lava rocks. Strangely, it is absent from Floreana and Tower islands. Plaza is perhaps a little too small to support a pair.

Galapagos Hawk, *Buteo galapagoensis*

Galapagos Dove, *Zenaida galapagoensis*

GALAPAGOS DOVE, *Zenaida galapagoensis*

The pigeons and doves, COLUMBIDAE, are easy to differentiate from all other bird groups. They are short-necked, stout, medium-sized birds, which fly well with much wing movement. Their beaks are characteristic, being moderately short, slender and somewhat thinner in the middle. The nostrils emerge through the basal fleshy cere. The feathers are only loosely attached to the skin, falling out quite easily. They are mostly vegetable feeders.

The Galapagos Dove is a ground dove, and is found where the ground is rocky or stony. It cannot be confused with any other species, as it is the only dove to be found in the Galapagos. It is endemic, most abundant and extraordinarily tame. The upper surface is dull reddish-brown, whilst underneath it is rosy-beige. A black band runs along the side of the body. The feet are red. Three characteristics easily observed are the irridescent patch on the side of the neck, the turquoise ring around the eyes and the white band on the wings when in flight. It is found on most of the islands.

Mocking Birds

The first birds seen on making a landing on almost every island of the Galapagos are the mocking birds. They are very tame, the tamest of all the islands' birds, and half a dozen are soon clustering around one's feet. The mocking birds of the Galapagos have been classified into four species which belong to the exclusively New World family MIMIDAE, containing thirty or so species of mocking birds, catbirds and thrashers. This group of birds is well known for its powers of mimicking the sounds and songs of other birds, but many of them are fine songsters themselves. They are very active and aggressive and usually do not move far away from the shrub layer. The family is placed between the wrens (TROGLODYTIDAE) and the thrushes (TURDIDAE).

The Galapagos mocking birds bear a great resemblance to the mocking bird of the southern United States and Mexico, *Mimus polyglottor*. In size and general appearance it is like a smallish, slender British Song Thrush, but with a longer slender tail and longer sharp beak. It is light greyish-brown with a white bar on the wings and a whitish breast.

The four species are given below; there are a number of sub-species.

Nesomimus trifasciatus, Charles
N. *macdonaldi*, Hood
N. *melanotis*, Chatham
N. *parvulus*, Albemarle, Narborough, Indefatigable, Barrington, Bindloe, Abingdon, James, Jervis and Wenman

VERMILION FLYCATCHER, Pyrocephalus rubinus

The male of this 14 cm (5½ in) bird is probably the most vividly coloured of all the Galapagos animals. It is not endemic, but is found in a wide range of shrubby habitats from the south-western United States to Argentina, but in the special, often drab, environment of the Galapagos it stands out like a gorgeously-garbed ruby. Its relative tameness and inquisitiveness impress every visitor to Galapagean shores. The female lacks the vivid coloration of her consort; instead of the vermilion crown and underparts, she is yellow with a brown back and wings. This beautiful little bird is found on most of the islands.

LARGE-BILLED FLYCATCHER, Myiarchas magnirostris

The tyrant flycatchers, TYRANNIDAE, to which this species belongs, is exclusively New World in distribution. The family shows great adaptability, although they are most plentiful in tropical lowlands and it is in this type of habitat that our present species can be observed. The coastal areas of the Galapagos are mostly inhospitable, but the Large-Billed Flycatcher appears to make a good living.

YELLOW WARBLER, Dendroica petechia

This small, bright yellow bird is a typical warbler in shape and behaviour. It has a small sharp beak with which it picks up insects as it continually hops and flutters its way through scrub and shrubs. The male is identified by its possession of bright chestnut-brown marks on the head and breast.

SHORT-EARED OWL, Asio flammeus

Of the 133 species of owl found in the world, two are present in the Galapagos. The Short-eared Owl is one of the most widely distributed species, being circumpolar in the northern hemisphere and

Vermilion Flycatcher, *Pyrocephalus rubinus*

Yellow Warbler, *Dendroica petechia*

Short-eared Owl, *Asio flammeus*

occurring in South America, as well as a number of oceanic islands. The northern populations are migratory so that its presence on remote islands is not unexpected. Generally, in various parts of the world, it feeds on anything alive it can catch and in the Galapagos its prey consists of both land and sea birds, as well as rats. It nests on the ground and often hunts during daytime. It should be looked for in the highlands and also in coastal areas near sea-bird nesting colonies and often roosts in tree cactus.

BARN OWL, *Tyto alba*

Owls are characterized by the presence of large facial discs and forward-facing eyes. In the Barn Owl the discs give the appearance of a mask. This species also is widely distributed, occurring in North and South America, Africa, South-east Asia, Arabia, Europe, Australia and Tasmania. It does not migrate.

The Barn Owl is placed in a different family (TYTONIDAE) from the Short-eared Owl (STRIGIDAE). The facial discs are heart-shaped and it has long, completely feathered legs. The face, belly and legs are white, whilst the upper parts are golden-brown, spangled and barred with white, grey and black. Its food is mainly rats and mice which it hunts only at night. Its presence is mostly noted from its long-drawn-out scream at night. It is a bird closely associated with man, attracted, no doubt, by man's rodent companions, and it often nests in old deserted buildings, usually keeping to the same one year after year, unless molested. In the Galapagos it is to be found in the central islands.

GALAPAGOS MARTIN, *Progne modesta*

The Galapagos Martin is an endemic subspecies of a species widely distributed in South America. The male is completely blue-black, similar to the closely related Purple Martin, *P. rubis*, of North America, but the female is greyish underneath and shows a faint collar. When flying it cannot be mistaken for any other Galapagos bird. It alternates gliding, when its sharp-pointed wings become visible, with periods of flapping as it regains height. It is seen around cliffs but is an unobtrusive bird, never in numbers and is uncommon.

DARK-BILLED CUCKOO, *Coccyzus melacoryphus*

This retiring bird is identical with the species found in South America and congeneric with the well known Yellow-billed and

Black-billed cuckoos of North America. All these are members of the sub-family PHOENICOPHAEINAE in which no members are parasitic. A flimsy twig nest is built where eggs are laid and where both parents take part in rearing the young. The dark-billed Cuckoo is dark grey on the top of the head and the back of the neck, the rest of the upper parts being greyish-brown banded with black-and-white markings. Underneath, it is light reddish.

COMMON GALLINULE, *Gallinula chloropus*

This bird is distributed throughout all the continents except Australia, and found almost everywhere its habitat occurs (marsh, stream and lakeside). This is the Moorhen of Europe, although the subspecies occurring in the Galapagos, *cachinnans*, is the one found on the American continent. It is one of the world's most widely distributed birds.

It is of medium size, dark brown above, purplish beneath, with the base of the beak and frontal shield sealing-wax red, but the tip of the beak is yellow. There is a white line along the side under the wings and the tail is white underneath. The legs and toes are long, green and not webbed. It flicks its tail sharply, showing a white patch, from time to time.

The Common Gallinule occurs in the wet highlands of the larger islands as well as in the region of Villamil on Albemarle.

BLACK RAIL, *Laterallus jamaicensis*

The family RALLIDAE which includes the rails, gallinules and coots, consists of small to medium-sized running, wading or swimming birds. Usually they are sombre in colour but not without exception and match their background. They appear to fly weakly although some migrate over long distances. Species of rail have populated almost all the larger islands, as well as many of the small ones. Island isolation has caused them to develop along lines suiting the specific environment and because of this many have become flightless.

The bodies of rails are laterally compressed and their legs are strong, enabling them to force a way through dense grass or undergrowth. The Black Rail belongs to a group with conical, shorter beaks, and is dark in colour with some chestnut on its back and spotted wings.

When disturbed, the Black Rail seeks escape by running, but may jump into the air and flutter for a metre or so before dashing into the undergrowth again. The young run about as soon as they are hatched, like small balls of black, animated cotton-wool. The species is endemic.

WHITE-CHEEKED PINTAIL DUCK, Anas bahamensis

Otherwise known as the Galapagos Pintail, it is a subspecies of the Bahamas Pintail. It is brown, dappled with lighter brown, and has conspicuous white cheeks. The 'speculum' is seen as a green patch on the wings when in flight. This is the only breeding species of the ANATIDAE in the Galapagos, and small flocks are usually to be seen in the crater lakes in fresh and salt water, as well as in many lagoons, such as that of Jervis. It is generally common.

BUFF-BACKED HERON, Bubulcus ibis

Also known as the Cattle Egret, in 1972 a flock of these small white herons (with a rusty-buff patch on crown and back) was seen amongst the cattle at Bella Vista on Santa Cruz during the breeding season.

During the last fifty years or so the Cattle Egret has invaded and populated whole continents where it was never seen before. Originating from North Africa and southern Eurasia, it is now found over a large part of North and South America, as well as Australia. It is usually found amongst grazing cattle feeding on insects and other small animals which have been disturbed. These birds often perch on the backs of the cattle.

Darwin's Finches

Perhaps the most characteristic group of land birds on the Galapagos are the finches. They are of exceptional interest to ornithologists and to students of evolution from all over the world. There are thirteen species, usually placed in the subfamily GEOSPIZINAE of the finch family FRINGILLIDAE. They are usually called Darwin's finches because Darwin was the first to point out that, although they are all closely related on anatomical grounds, their beaks show significant differences in shape and function.

It seemed obvious to Darwin that, by some means, a population of a single species of (ancestral) finch had somehow arrived in the non-bird-populated Galapagos, and that, in the search for ecological

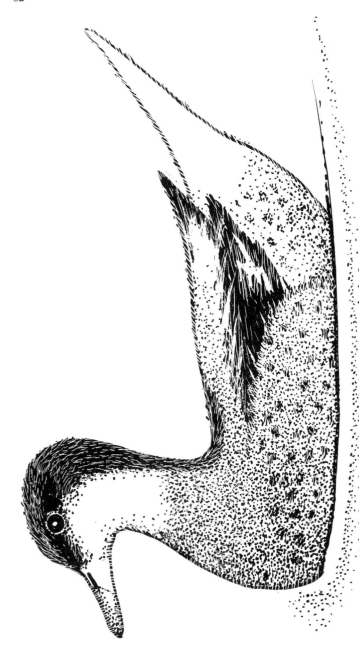

White-cheeked or Bahama Pintail Duck, *Anas bahamensis*

(1) Large Ground Finch, *Geospiza magnirostris*
(2) Medium Ground Finch, *Geospiza fortis*
(3) Small Ground Finch, *Geospiza fulginosa*
(4) Warbler Finch, *Certhidea olivacea*
(5) Large Cactus Ground Finch, *Geospiza conirostris*
(6) Cactus Ground Finch, *Geospiza scandens*
(7) Sharp-billed Ground Finch, *Geospiza difficilis*
(8) Woodpecker Finch, *Cactospiza pallida*
(9) Vegetarian Finch, *Platyspiza crassirostris*
(10) Mangrove Finch, *Cactospiza heliobates*
(11) Medium Tree Finch, *Camarhynchus pauper*
(12) Large Tree Finch, *Camarhynchus psittacula*
(13) Small Tree Finch, *Camarhynchuss parvulus*

'niches', groups of the species had become adapted to seeking out rather specialized food. All the Galapagos finches are drab, sparrow-sized birds with dusty, rather rough-and-tumble feathering. Like sparrows, too, some species appear to be equally at home underneath the tea-table searching for crumbs, or in the open countryside extracting their natural food from cultivated crops or wild nature. They are confiding and can be called readily by the observer making clicking noises by drawing in air through clenched teeth and releasing it with the tongue. If the observer is partially hidden in the scrub the finches will come flocking in to investigate the unfamiliar noise.

The subfamily GEOSPIZINAE is divided into five genera. In *Geospiza*, the six species are finch-like in that they feed mainly on, or near, the ground, mostly on seeds, but with a few insects. The beaks of the different species show a graduation in size according to the size and hardness of the seeds on which they subsist. The Large Ground Finch, *G. magnirostris*, possesses a large strong bill and feeds on hard seeds of relatively few species. The Medium Ground Finch, *G. fortis*, has a smaller beak and feeds on moderately hard seeds of a much larger number of species, whilst the Small Ground Finch, *G. fuliginosa*, feeds on a large number of different sorts of seeds and its bill is much smaller. The Sharp-billed Ground Finch, *G. difficilis*, has an elongate, thin, sharp beak and, although its feeding habits are not well known, it might subsist on insects. The Cactus Ground Finch, *G. scandens*, has a stouter bill than *G. difficilis*, and, although it feeds on a few species of moderately hard seeds, it prefers to feed on the fruits and nectar of *Opuntia* cactus. Its semi-dependence on the cactus tree has resulted in it being more arboreal than its congeners. It also builds its nest on the *Opuntia* cactus. The Large-billed or Large Cactus Ground Finch, *G. conirostris*, feeds on various seeds, soft and hard, but also on the soft *Opuntia* tissue. Its bill is large, as long as that of *G. magnirostris*, but not nearly so deep, so it cannot tackle seeds of the degree of hardness with which *G. magnirostris* can deal.

Placed in the genus *Camarhynchus* are the three species known as Tree finches. The Parrot-billed or Large Tree Finch, *C. psittacula*, has a large, laterally compressed, hooked bill and feeds on a variety of largish insects which it excavates from twigs and branches, as well as taking a few seeds. The Medium Tree Finch, *C. pauper*, has a beak smaller than the previous species but still similar in shape.

Its food is presumed to be intermediate between that of the previous species and that of the following.

The Small Tree Finch, C. *parvulus*, again has a similar shaped beak to the two previous species, but it is much smaller. It feeds on a wide variety of smallish insects and a moderate amount of soft seeds.

The most remarkable genus, however, is *Cactospiza*, consisting of two species. The Woodpecker Finch, C. *pallida*, has a strong, largish, though slender, beak, which it uses much as does a woodpecker. It pecks at the bark of trees in order to find the tunnels of wood-boring beetle larvae (such as those of the CERAMBYCIDAE) and other insects sheltering in the tunnels. When it detects an insect, if possible it takes it out with its beak, but if this is impossible the bird is not defeated; it fetches a cactus spine or something similar and, holding it in its beak, uses it as a tool in order to extract the food. Examples of the use of tools by birds are rare, so this is all the more remarkable in that this special behaviour could only have been developed within the last few million years. The Woodpecker possesses a long, spiny tongue, actuated by strong muscles, absent, of course, in the Woodpecker Finch. However, the Woodpecker Finch also feeds on soft fruit and seeds, so that feeding behaviour is still in a plastic state.

The Mangrove Finch, C. *heliobates*, feeds on insects in mangroves, but little is known about it.

The Vegetarian Finch, *Platyspiza crassirostris*, has a sharp-pointed, down-curved, angled bill. It feeds on a variety of vegetable matter, including buds, leaves, flowers, fleshy fruits and seeds both hard and soft. Its feeding manner is slow and leisurely, as in the case of many other birds of like habit.

The Warbler Finch, *Certhidea olivacea*, feeds only on small insects which it finds on leaves, branches, etc. It picks them off with its small, slender, acute bill. It is found from the coastal, arid zone to the high, moist zone.

CHAPTER 6

Birds of Sea and Shore

WAVED ALBATROSS, *Diomedea irrorata*

Of the thirteen species of albatross, one of them, the Waved Albatross, is endemic to the Galapagos. It has been estimated that there are about ten thousand of them and all breed on Hood, the most south-easterly island of the Galapagos. When not breeding, the birds winter above the fauna-rich waters of the Humboldt Current as it sweeps northwards up the coasts of Colombia, Peru and Ecuador.

The Waved Albatross is a large bird; barnyard goose size with a wing-span of up to 2·5 m (8 ft). This compares with the 3·3 m (11 ft) wing-span of the Wandering Albatross, the bird with the longest wings in the world.

The albatrosses, or DIOMEDEIDAE, are large birds with spectacularly long, narrow wings. A special anatomical feature which they share with the petrels and shearwaters is the extension of the nostrils into a tube on top of the beak. Except in the breeding season they spend all their time soaring and gliding over the oceans. They require stiff blowing conditions to help them keep aloft and the Equator (the Doldrum), is a barrier to their distribution. Seldom, if ever, do they cross it, but the Humboldt Current, turning to the west as it reaches the Equator, causes climatic conditions which produce enough breeze for the Waved Albatross to come within a few kilometres of the equator to breed. Mostly albatrosses are to be found between the tropic of Capricorn and the Antarctic circle, but three species are found in the North Pacific and more in the North Atlantic.

The Waved Albatross is white with a brown-grey back, and the back of the head has a yellowish tinge. The massive 15 cm (6 in)

Waved Albatross, *Diomedea irrorata*

long beak is also yellow, whilst the eye, and a narrow ring surrounding it, are blackish. There are mottled (waved) feathers around the base of the neck.

The breeding areas on Hood Island are shrubby and littered with rough, reddish rock which makes landing and take-off hazardous and there are a number of mishaps, but the area is on the top of high cliff and the upsurging wind currents make take-off possible.

Frigate Birds

Around the coasts of the Galapagos, the frigate birds are seldom out of sight. In numbers they may vary from a couple of specks in the sky—where they will be watching the boobies fishing so that they might harry and persecute them in order to rob them—to up to a hundred flying only a metre or so above mast height. They possess extraordinary eyesight, watching each other from long distances, because, when a few fish are thrown overboard, within a few minutes they appear as if by magic!

Of all the sea birds they have the greatest powers of flight. They soar for hours at a time, yet in a second can dive towards the unattended chick of a nesting booby, or fly rings around a booby, returning with a fish caught far out at sea, until it gives it up. The frigate bird catches it long before it drops into the sea. However, only some 30 per cent of its food is obtained by robbery, the remainder being picked up from the surface of the ocean with its long beak.

The wings of frigate birds are very long, narrow and pointed and have a span of 2·5 m (8 ft). The tail is long and strongly swallow-tailed. In spite of the fact that their feet are webbed and that they spend all their time flying over water, they never settle or dive into it. Their feathers quickly get waterlogged and they are not able to fly off. Even on land they have great difficulty in taking off unless settled on a bush, mangrove or steep cliff.

The breeding season of frigate birds is remarkable for the courtship. During most of the year the male has an orange patch on the throat; in the breeding season, however, it becomes deep crimson and he periodically inflates the gular pouch which makes it look like a toy balloon. The male sits on the nest, inflating his pouch to attract suitable females until they pair. Incubation is shared, as the egg, or single chick, is never left alone as otherwise it would soon

Great Frigate Bird, *Fregata minor*, female

be gobbled up by a neighbour. Female frigate birds are slightly larger and lighter in colour than the males.

In the Galapagos two species of frigate bird occur. These are the Magnificent Frigate Bird, *Fregata magnificens*, and the Great Frigate Bird, *Fregata minor*. Of all birds they have the greater ratio of wing-span to bodyweight, the latter being no more than about 1.5 kg (3 lb). The Magnificent Frigate Bird is not normally to be seen attending the booby colonies, but prefers to pick up what it can around the fishing villages. The male is an irridescent purple black, whilst the female is whitish underneath, with a black throat. The Great Frigate Bird, is black with a brown band on the wings, whilst the female is white underneath without the black throat of the female magnificent bird.

The incubation period is so long (fifty-five days) that breeding cannot take place on an annual cycle. In addition, the parent birds change over during incubation only at about ten-day intervals, so that they forgo feeding for quite lengthy intervals. Indeed, they lose about one-fifth of their bodyweight during this period. One of the chief breeding areas on the Galapagos is Tower Island where it occurs from April to June.

Boobies

The nine species of boobies and gannets are classified in the family SULIDAE. They consist of goose-sized birds (from which the generic name of the boobies derives—*Sula*) with long, heavy, wedge-shaped beaks and sharp-pointed tails. The wings are long and also sharp-pointed. Internally they are insulated from their heavy impacts with water by an air-sac network beneath the skin. Whilst the three species of gannets are inhabitants of temperate waters, the six species of booby are found in the tropics.

Three booby species are found in Galapagos waters. Indeed, it is seldom that one or more species are out of sight if one is on the shore, or sailing along the coast. These species are as follows.

BLUE-FOOTED BOOBY, *Sula nebouxii*

The most striking feature which this species possesses is the bright blue colour of its feet. They are so much like two pieces of blue plastic that it is almost unbelievable! It is the most abundant of the three species and, as it normally feeds fairly close inshore, it is the

Blue-footed Booby, *Sula nebouxii*

most frequently observed. The wings are brown, the feathers of the back brown, edged with white, whilst the head and neck are finely mottled white-and-brown. The beak is dark bluey-black whilst the eyes are very conspicuous and, strangely, they present us with a rare type of secondary sexual character. The dark pigmented area around the pupil is much larger in the female than in the male. In addition, she honks and he whistles. They are colonial nesters in such areas being close to the shore, such as the two craters of Daphne. They nest on the ground with but a few stones to mark the nesting area. Three chicks are sometimes raised but more often two or one depending on food supply. However, because of their inshore feeding, they are more often in attendance on the young which contrasts with the single chick raised by the other two booby species.

MASKED BOOBY, *Sula dactylatra*

With a wing-span of 1·5 m (5½ ft), this is the largest of the Galapagos boobies. Head and body are of an intense whiteness, making them visible over large distances—like the Gannet of the North Atlantic. The outer part of the wings and the tail, however, are almost black. The legs and feet are a slatey-grey, whilst the beak is creamy-yellow but with black-and-grey markings at the base, the masking. The conspicuous eyes are orange. It nests in small colonies, often near to one of the Blue-footed Boobies, but mostly is to be found on steep hillsides or near cliffs. Only one of the two chicks reaches the adult stage. This is probably related to the distance from its feeding grounds, as these are seldom near the coast. Small groups are often seen several kilometres from the coast.

RED-FOOTED BOOBY, *Sula sula*

This is the smallest booby found in the Galapagos. The beak is blue, but pink or reddish at the base, whilst the legs and feet are sealing-wax red. Two colour phases of the plumage occur. One is brown and the other is white, with the exception of the outer wing which is black. The latter body coloration could be mistaken for a Masked Booby but the blue beak should put its identity beyond doubt.

The Red-Footed Booby, unlike the other two species, nests in trees or shrubs but appears to avoid the larger central islands. The largest colony in the Galapagos is that of Tower Island where an estimated 140,000 pairs occur. Here, the nests, which are about 1·5 m (6 ft) apart, are made of twigs, with or without green leaves,

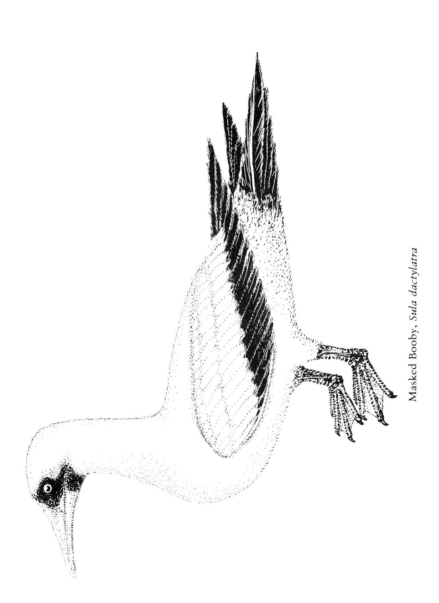

Masked Booby, *Sula dactylatra*

and the male defends his territory by waggling his head and scream-
ing defiance. One egg only is laid and the incubation period is forty-
six days.

Elsewhere in the world it is generally distributed throughout the
tropical oceans as is the Masked Booby, but the Blue-footed Booby
is confined to the tropical eastern Pacific, from Mexico to Peru.

All boobies and gannets feed by diving! This is often from spec-
tacular heights so their eyesight must be exceptionally keen. Frequently whole flocks feed simultaneously when a large school of
fish has been located. The birds hit the water with considerable
force, sending up showers of spray. They usually remain underwater
for a few seconds only, but they sometimes pursue their prey underwater and one has been recorded as being caught in a fishing net
27 m (90 ft) under the surface. It is usually supposed that the fish
is swallowed underwater, but in an excellent series of photographs,
taken by A. Bamford, of the Gannet, one is shown with a large fish
in its beak, swallowing it on the surface. In addition, when boobies
are cruising in front of the bows of a ship, waiting for flying fish
to be disturbed, they catch them just as they regain the water. The
booby juggles with the fish for a moment then swallows it.

When gannets and boobies enter the water from a dive, and also
when they swim underwater, they hold their wings folded back so
that they touch almost along the whole length, except the primary
feathers. The upper arm (humerus) is first held against the body
whilst the rest of the wing forms a plane. An extraordinary example
of the variable geometry of a bird's wing.

THE RED-BILLED TROPIC BIRD, *Phaeton aethereus*

The pair of long, trailing tail-feathers of the tropic birds make them
unmistakable. It is only in the tropics that they occur. The species
around the Galapagos is the Red-billed, and it breeds there all the
year round, with the exception of the island Plazas where it breeds
only in August and September. Only one egg is laid, in a shallow
hole usually with a rocky roof. Usually a number of pairs appear
to nest in any one particular area, but they do not actually nest in
colonies. It feeds in the manner of the booby, flying rather purposely
about 15 m (50 ft) above the sea, then suddenly diving into it in order
to catch surface-swimming fish or squid.

The Red-billed Tropic Bird is about the size of a seagull but it
has an altogether different flight and general habit. It is mostly white

Red-billed Tropic Bird, *Phaeton aethereus*

Flightless Cormorant, *Nannopterum harrisi*

with a black eye and bar from the eye to the back of the head. The back is attractively barred with an almost bluey-black, reminiscent of a Silver Pheasant, especially with its long tail-feathers. The outer primary feathers are black.

FLIGHTLESS CORMORANT, *Nannopterum harrisi*

About 800 pairs of this strange endemic bird remain and they are found only around the Narborough and Albemarle coastlines. It is of typical cormorant appearance and is of goose size. The plumage is dark brown, almost blackish and has a shaggy appearance, especially when wet. The short legs are stout and very strong. The eyes are pale bluish-grey. The wings, however, have lost their function, the bird not only being unable to fly, but does not use them underwater when it is searching for, and chasing, fish or squid. Propulsion underwater is by vigorous thrusts of its webbed feet.

The Flightless Cormorant breeds at any time of the year at traditional sites which are usually rocky slabs close to sheltered coves, mostly within a few metres of the water. Several pairs invariably nest together and the area is white with their droppings. The nest itself is a hollow in the rock with a few bits of dried seaweed and pebbles. It is exceptionally tame when sitting. It normally lays a clutch of two or three eggs. The young are fed by regurgitation thrusting their sharp beaked heads down the throat of the parent.

It swims on the surface of the sea with the body submerged and, when it comes ashore, mounts an outstanding rock to dry its wings, just as a flying cormorant species would.

GALAPAGOS PENGUIN, *Spheniscus mendiculus*

The Galapagos Penguin, although not the smallest species of penguin (that honour goes to the Fairy Penguin, *Eudyptula minor*, of Australia, Tasmania and New Zealand), is the smallest of the *Spheniscus* group. It is characterized by the long and slender beak, a very narrow, white head-stripe, and the flippers being almost entirely black.

Although the Galapagos Penguin is found from time to time on a number of the islands, it is most likely to be seen around the shores of Fernandina and Isabela, being the only two islands where they breed. It is only recently that their breeding sites have been discovered, usually in a tunnel-like cavity amongst the lava slabs near the water's edge, in company with the Flightless Cormorant. The

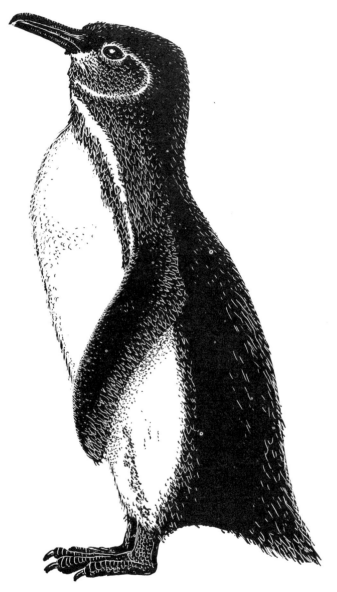

Galapagos Penguin, *Spheniscus mendiculus*

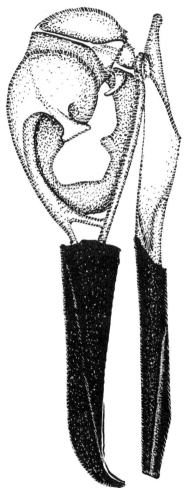

Skull of Galapagos Penguin

total population is between 1,000 and 2,000 and is thus the most rare of all penguin species and lies near the extinction danger line. Because of their great rarity, the eggs are often stolen. The breeding season is from May to July, but the present writer has seen incubating birds in October.

The Galapagos Penguin, like many other Galapagos birds, is very tame and, when swimming close to the shore, it is often attracted to the water's edge by the imitation of its call. It swims on the surface with its head, only, above water and when submerged propels itself with its flippers only. The feet are situated, as in all penguins, at the hinder end of the body, although they take no part in swimming, and give the penguins their upright stance when out of the water. There are fifteen species of penguin in the world and they are classified in the family SPHENISCIDAE. They are found only in the southern hemisphere. The Galapagos Penguin has the most northerly distribution of all, reaching the Equator. Generally, penguins are associated with the cold waters of the Antarctic and it seems reasonable to suppose that it was the cold Humboldt Current from the Antarctic that brought the penguin to the Galapagos in the first place, and, being rich in organisms, enables them to remain.

Penguins are specially adapted to spend most of their time in the sea. They have lost the power of flight but the 'wings' are modified to become efficient fins or flippers. The body is streamlined for swimming and they exceed speeds of 40 kmph (25 mph) under water. The flippers have no joints and are only moved from the shoulder.

Gulls and Terns

Gulls and terns are easy to identify. They have long narrow wings and webbed feet, and are closely related to the skuas, the piratical birds that prey on them, but the gulls do not possess the cere, the wax-like upper sheath. Gulls are not, as a rule, found very far from land so that the endemic Lava Gulls, or rather their forebears, when blown to the Galapagos in some raging storm, have stayed closely linked to the islands. Perhaps the same can be said of the Swallow-tailed Gull except, of course, it bears no distinct difference from the same species on the South American coast.

LAVA OR DUSKY GULL, Larus fuliginosus

This gull is easy to identify, having a black head with beak and feet of the same colour. Each eye is conspicuously encircled with white. The rest of the body is a dull sooty-grey. When yawning the throat is seen to be a deep purplish-crimson.

Closely related to the Laughing Gull of the American mainland, it makes a similar call much like cackling human laughter. However, the Lava Gull is one of the world's rarest birds as there are only about 400 pairs. It is usually seen singly or in pairs, pecking along the shoreline for crabs and marine debris of various kinds, but it will take small Marine Iguanas.

A rough nest of sticks is made in which two olive-green eggs are laid. Watch out—for it defends its nest with vigour. Ordinarily they are confiding birds, flying out to welcome ships into the anchorage.

SWALLOW-TAILED GULL, Greagus furcatus

This beautiful gull is found around the coastline of a number of Galapagos islands where there are rocky cliffs, even if not very high. The back and wings are of the palest smoky-grey, with underparts almost white. The head is dark grey with the large, lustrous eyes ringed with red. The beak is black with a white tip and white also at the base of the upper mandible. Most noticeable in flight is the white, forked tail.

It arrives at the Galapagos to breed and its single egg is generally laid on a rocky ledge or on flat ground. Its only other known breeding place is Malpelo Island off the Colombian coast.

The Swallow-tailed Gull is a night feeder, feeding on fish and squid that come to the surface, and when not breeding is found along the coastline of Peru and Ecuador.

BROWN NODDY, Anous stolidus

The noddies are those terns more exclusively tropical in distribution than the terns commonly so-called. They are referred to as noddies on account of their habit of bowing and nodding when greeting at the nest.

The Brown Noddy is identified by its general sooty-brown colour, with frosty-grey cap, white eyelids and a longish, wedge-shaped tail. When perching, it has a graceful streamlined appearance which, with its long curved beak, make it easy to identify. It obtains its

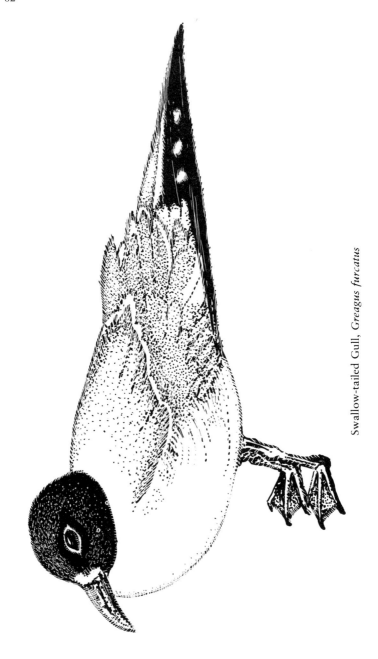

Swallow-tailed Gull, *Greagus furcatus*

food, usually small fish, by picking it up from the surface of the sea. A small nest is made of dried grass on a ledge of a cliff-face, and a single egg is laid. A number of birds on their nest sites can usually be seen at the entrance to the cave, Roca Vincente, on Isabela.

Altogether there are thirty-nine different species of tern, characterized by their slender streamlined shape, long, narrow, pointed wings and their beaks which are long and sharp-pointed. The legs of terns are shorter than those of gulls.

The Brown Noddy ranges far and wide, being found in tropical areas of the Atlantic, Indian and Pacific Oceans.

SOOTY TERN, *Sterna fuscata*

The crown, back, wings, upper tail, beak and legs, are sooty-black, whilst the under parts are white. There is a white band on the forehead. The deeply forked tail and the long sharp beak are easily recognizable characteristics. The Sooty Tern is found throughout the tropical seas, although it generally does not rest on land like most tern species, except when breeding. In the Galapagos it nests in large numbers on Culpepper and appears to favour the warmer waters of the northern islands. Elsewhere it breeds on isolated islands of the Pacific, Atlantic and Indian Oceans, usually with the Brown Noddy, and often in colonies of large size. Only a single egg is laid, although tern species breeding in temperate regions lay more. In the Ascension Island in the Atlantic, the breeding cycle is ten months. It is often called the Wideawake.

THE BROWN PELICAN, *Pelicanus occidentalis*

The pelican is a bird well known to almost everyone, by virtue of its capacious gular pouch. It uses this as a dip-net when swimming on the surface, or when making a dive. This is known as a plunge-dive, because the pelican appears to come in from an angle and arrives on the water surface with a great flop. When a fish is caught, the water is drained away from the pouch before it is swallowed. It is very successful in catching small to medium-sized fish. Throughout the world there are six species of pelican and all are large birds, associated with freshwater lakes, estuaries and sheltered coasts. Usually pelicans are mostly white in colour, the exception being the Brown Pelican.

It has a wide distribution in the New World, occurring along the coasts of the southern United States, the West Indies and Venezuela,

Brown Pelican, *Pelicanus occidentalis*

Central America and the Pacific coast of Central and South America as far as Chile. The Brown Pelican is abundant in the Galapagos where it breeds in the mangrove-encircled lagoons. Two or three eggs are laid on a large, untidy twig-nest.

The Brown Pelican of the Galapagos has a white head, pink-rimmed eyes and a dark-coloured pouch. In breeding plumage there is a slight crest, and at the back of the neck, starting from the crest and finishing at its base, is a deep chestnut band. The body is grey-ish-brown and appears deepest well behind the legs. The feathers of the body have a strange scale-like appearance and the legs and webbed feet are dark slatish-grey-black in colour. The wing-span of the Brown Pelican is 2 m (6½ ft), whereas that of the larger white-coloured species is as much as 2·5 m (9 ft). In spite of their ability to make slantwise dives into the water, pelicans often look very un-gainly and have difficulties in taking off from water. In the Gala-pagos there are always large numbers of immature birds about, and although it is hazardous being a young pelican, large numbers appear as if by magic around a ship when fish scraps are being thrown overboard.

Petrels and Shearwaters

These two groups of sea birds are closely related to each other in the possession of a 'tube-nose'—the nostrils being situated at the end of a tube-like process on top of the beak. One shearwater, Audu-bon's Shearwater, *Puffinus iberminiensi*, is a common inhabitant of Galapagos waters. They are called shearwaters on account of their wave-skimming habit of flight. They do not normally follow in the wakes of ships.

The visitor is most likely to see this medium-sized, dull, black bird, with white underparts, wheeling around in noisy flocks near the bases of the cliffs where they breed; this occurs every nine or ten months. Most shearwaters are known to possess extraordinary migration habits, involving outstanding direction-finding sense.

A single egg is laid in a burrow or tunnel in the rocks.

Four species of storm petrel are found in Galapagos waters. They are small birds, spending all their time, except for breeding, flutter-ing with quick wing beats, interspersed with short glides, over the ocean. Indeed, they are the smallest of pelagic birds. None of the storm petrels exceeds 25 cm (10 in) in length.

WHITE-VESTED or ELLIOT'S STORM PETREL,
Oceanites gracilis

This is the only one of the four species found in the Galapagos or the surrounding waters which is endemic and, although it breeds in the islands, its nesting sites have never been found. This is the common species seen from the shore and the white line running down the breast and under the tail, and its longish legs, distinguish it from other species. Its flight is characteristic. It flies very close to the water and does not make sudden direction changes.

GALAPAGOS or WEDGE-RUMPED STORM PETREL,
Oceanodroma tethys

Two breeding colonies of this storm petrel are known in the Galapagos. Nearly a quarter of a million pairs are stated to nest on Tower Island and there is a breeding colony at Point Pitt at the north-eastern tip of San Cristobal. There is also a possibility that it breeds on Redonda Rock, to the north west of Point Albemarle on Isabela Island. This species is distinguished by the triangular white area on the rump. Its behaviour is unlike that of other species in that it feeds at night and visits its nest during daytime. Its flight is erratic.

MADEIRAN or BAND-RUMPED STORM PETREL,
Oceanodroma castro

This species is distinguished by the square white patch on the rump. It is slightly larger than the two foregoing species and breeds on the smaller islands of the Galapagos. It is an oceanic feeder and is rarely seen, visiting its nest only at night.

HAWAIIAN or DARK-RUMPED PETREL,
Pterodroma phoepygia

This species has no white on the upper surface except a white forehead, and the wings are white underneath. It nests in deep-dug burrows in the central highlands of the larger islands, but, as it visits its nest only at night, it, too, is rarely seen.

GREAT BLUE HERON, Ardea herodias

The heron family ARDEIDAE, which also includes the bitterns and egrets, includes sixty-two species of which four, probably five, are to be seen in the Galapagos. Herons possess long bills, long necks and long legs, all adaptations to wading along shores, tide-pools and marshes where they catch a wide variety of animal life. Herons are notable for the large amount of powder-down which they produce. This is a product of the fraying ends of non-moulting feathers which grow on paired patches on the breast, flanks and rump. It is used by the bird for cleaning up its feathers after a slimy fish has been caught.

The Great Blue Heron stands about 1·5 m (52 in) high, and its size makes it unmistakable. It is blue-grey, with lighter head and a long black crest. The front of the neck is longitudinally barred with black. It is a colonial nester and is distributed widely in North and Central America, as well as in the West Indies. In the Galapagos it is said to enter houses for food.

LAVA HERON, *Butorides sundevalli*

This endemic species is known also as the Galapagos Green Heron and belongs to the group called the 'day herons'.

It stands no more than 50 cm (20 in) high and, although its legs are long, it has a hunched appearance as the neck is short and it commonly rests its head between its shoulders. It is dark bluish-green above and paler beneath, and is common along the lava-lined shores, fishing for small crabs and other marine prey.

YELLOW-CROWNED NIGHT HERON, *Nyctanassa violacea*

Distributed throughout North and South America, this relatively small heron is mottled-grey in colour with a black head ornamented with white or yellow on the crown, a broad white bar behind the eye, and a nuchal crest. Although it is seen in statuesque rigidity, watching for small crustacea and fish in tide pools in daylight, it is mainly nocturnal. It stands 71 cm (28 in) high.

BLACK-NECKED STILT, *Himantopus mexicanus*

Commonly seen wading in both salt- and freshwater lagoons, this exceptionally slender member of the family SCOLOPACIDAE, is easily recognized by its very long, red legs, long, thin, black beak and black crown, back of neck and all upper parts. Elsewhere the body is gleaming white. It swims readily and when in flight the legs trail behind the tail.

Yellow-crowned Night Heron, *Nyctanassa violacea*

AMERICAN OYSTERCATCHER, *Haematopus palliatus*

Very similar in appearance to the European Oystercatcher, this medium-sized and conspicuous bird has a brilliant carmine beak, pink legs and red-ringed, yellow eyes. The forepart of the head and body is a glossy black, the rest of the upper parts are brown, and the underparts white. It is usually seen singly, or in pairs, searching amongst the lava blocks at low tide for molluscs, which it will knock off the rocks and break open with its chisel-like beak. When disturbed, it flies off with a loud whistle of penetrating shrillness.

COMMON EGRET, *Casmerodius albus*

This all-white, heron-like bird is about 1 m (40 in) in length. It has a yellow beak, with black legs and feet. It is easily identified in flight, as it holds its head close against its shoulders with its long neck looped beneath. The wings are broad and rounded and the flight is slow. During the breeding season the well known plumes, known as 'aigrettes', are produced which were much sought after as decoration for ladies' hats until many countries protected the birds. It mainly inhabits the coastal areas where it feeds both on land animals, such as lizards and grasshoppers, and fish from the tide pools.

CHAPTER 7

Migrant Birds

Many birds that breed in the North American continent fly south in autumn to spend the winter under more temperate, even tropical, conditions, before flying north again to breed in the spring. In their migration flights many birds appear to follow the Pacific coastline so that, as the shore goes towards the east, obviously many birds wanting to make south will fly over the open ocean and many reach the Galapagos. M. P. Harris has given a list of twenty-nine birds of such species, eleven of which are regularly seen. The greater proportion are associated with shore or sea.

Contrasting with the extreme tameness of the endemic species, the migrants require to be approached with great caution for identification. When walking along the beaches, peer carefully over the headlands before clambering over them to the next beach. When visiting a lagoon, look through the mangroves whilst making a way through them, and do not walk into the open. Do not talk, nor make any sudden movement.

BLACK-BELLIED PLOVER, *Squatarola squatarola*

Plovers, CHARADRIIDAE, are small to medium-sized stoutish birds, usually with a distinctive colour pattern. The bill is straight, pigeon-like, slightly swollen towards the tip and always shorter than the head. The above species is about 30 cm (12 in) in length and has the lower parts of the face and the underparts of the body coal-black, whilst the upper parts are reticulated in brown and white. This is a bird of the Arctic tundra, and it migrates to Patagonia, South Africa and Australia.

SEMI-PALMATED PLOVER, *Charadrius semipalmatus*

This plover is only 17 cm (7 in) in length and is one of the group of 'ringed' plovers. It has a single black band across the white chest. It frequents the subarctic regions of North America and migrates to Patagonia.

WHIMBREL, *Numenius phaeopus*

The family SCOLOPACIDAE consists of eighty-two species of waders, of which the above is a good example. It has a long, thin, down-curved beak, long legs, and is brown marked with darker brown and black. It breeds in the tundra of North America, but spends the summer south of the Equator.

WANDERING TATTLER, *Heteroscelus incanus*

Dark brown above, pale brown beneath, with a white eye-stripe, this medium-sized relative of the Whimbrel is often to be seen along the shore. It has a long, down-curved bill like the Whimbrel, but the legs are yellow. It breeds in the Arctic tundra.

RUDDY TURNSTONE, *Arenaria interpres*

This stoutish 22 cm (9 in) long wader has rusty patches on the upper parts and a wide black patch across the breast. Its legs are red, but when flying it appears to be wholly black and white. Common along rocky shores.

SANDERLING, *Crocethia alba*

This very pale-coloured, almost white, wader belongs to the Sand-piper group EROLIINAE. It prefers sandy shores. In flight a black mark on the bend of the wings identifies it. It is circumpolar in breeding distribution, but migrates as far as Australia and New Zealand for the polar winter.

NORTHERN PHALAROPE, *Phalaropus pobatus*

Three species of phalarope constitute the PHALAROPODIDAE. The above species is small (20 cm, 8 in) and dainty, with a thin, pointed beak. As well as wading, it swims buoyantly and jerkily, often gyrating in order to stir up small organisms. As an adaption to this the toes are lobed. It nests in the Arctic tundra, where the male builds the nest, incubates the eggs and rears the young. It winters at sea, usually many kilometres from the coast in the southern regions of the Northern hemisphere.

The Red Phalarope, *Phalaropus fulicarius*, is also regularly seen in Galapagos waters. The whole of the underparts of the female are rusty-red in the breeding season, whilst the female of the Northern Phalarope has only a small rusty-red throat patch.

WILSON'S PHALAROPE, *Phalaropus tricolor*

Rusty-red along the sides of the neck and two wing bars of the same colour with a washed-out rusty neck, distinguish this larger species of phalarope. It breeds on marshes in the prairies of North America, and winters as far south as the Argentine pampas. It has a black eye-stripe. In the Galapagos the phalaropes are usually seen out at sea, either swimming—when they are very tame, allowing a close approach—or as a flock, wheeling around with the precision of a single organism.

FRANKLIN'S GULL *Larus pipixcan*

The black-tipped, grey wings of this otherwise white gull will identify this commonly seen bird, but it does not breed on the Galapagos. During the breeding season the head is hooded black, but in winter (when usually seen in the Galapagos) it is mottled-brown. Franklin's Gull nests around the edges of small lakes in the western prairies of Canada and the United States, and winters along South American coasts.

LEAST SANDPIPER, *Erolia minutilla*

The sandpipers are classified in the subfamily EROLIINAE. The above species is reddish-brown, marked with dark brown on top, with a white eye-stripe, whilst the breast is faintly marked with light brown spots. It is only 15 cm (6 in) in length. It breeds in boreal North America, but migrates to northern parts of South America. It is occasionally seen on beaches.

SPOTTED SANDPIPER, *Actitis macularia*

This sandpiper breeds within a large area of temperate North America, and winters as far south as Brazil and northern Chile. It is 20 cm (8 in) in length and dark greyish-brown on top with large crescent-shaped spots on the underparts.

THE SOLITARY SANDPIPER, Tringa solitaria

This species is not so frequently seen as the foregoing. It breeds in North America and is remarkable for laying its eggs in the abandoned nests of other birds.

SNOWY EGRET, Egretta thula

After a period of decline due to plume-hunting, the Snowy Egret is now relatively common from the central United States as far south as Argentina. It is snowy-white, much smaller than the Common Egret, and also differs from this species in having a substantial plumed crest. The legs are black and the feet are yellow.

BLUE-WINGED TEAL, Anas discors

The drake is easily identified by the head being dark grey-brown with a white crescent in front of the eye, and the speculum is metallic-green with a white band in front of it. The forewing is lapis lazuli blue, and that of the duck is only slightly duller. It is usually found in compact flocks and its flight is swift. It is mainly a surface feeder, and prefers small ponds during the breeding season; nesting takes place in the prairie regions of North America. It winters as far south as Chile and is often seen in the cattle ponds at Bueno Vista on Santa Cruz.

OSPREY, Pandion haliætus

One of the most widely distributed of all birds, the Osprey is found along most of the coastal waters or lakesides of the world, with the exception only of New Zealand. It feeds on fish which it catches, only occasionally accepting a freshly killed fish by some other agency. It is found in many oceanic islands. It sights its prety from the air, then plunges with half-closed wings on top of its prey which it grasps with its talons, often submerging completely. It grasps the fish with two toes in front and two behind, all toes being equal in length. In North America it nests along the entire length of both the Atlantic and Pacific coasts, as well as around inland lakes. In winter it migrates southwards, reaching the northern part of the South American continent.

PEREGRINE, Falco peregrinus

The Peregrine is another widely distributed bird, and like the Osprey is absent from New Zealand. The Peregrine possesses long, pointed wings, and another characteristic is the loose, large thigh feathers which give the appearance of trousers. When swooping on its prey it attains great speed, striking with its feet which usually break the prey's back. This is the bird often called the 'Duck Hawk' in North America. It nests on cliff ledges.

GREATER YELLOWLEGS, *Tringa melanoleuca*

This and the following three species are closely related to the tattlers and sandpipers. The Greater Yellowlegs is about 35 cm (14 in) in length with a long, straight bill, long, brilliant-yellow legs and the upper parts mottled and patterned in brown-and-white. It breeds in marshland in northern Canada and, although generally only coming as far south as the Gulf of Mexico for winter, it regularly turns up in the Galapagos.

LESSER YELLOWLEGS, *Tringa flavipes*

This is similar in habit and appearance to the Greater Yellowlegs but is about 25 cm (10 in) long and its call note differs.

WILLET *Catoptrophorus semipalmatus*

The numbers of the Large Grey Willet once dropped catastrophically, but it has now become abundant, due to protection. It breeds along the Atlantic coast of the United States. When flying, it reveals a conspicuous white patch on the wings. It likes to perch on posts, but is not likely to be seen doing this in the Galapagos!

SHORT-BILLED DOWITCHER, *Limnodromus griseus*

This light, rusty-brown bird has a long, straight bill and is 30 cm (12 in) in length. It breeds from Alaska to north Quebec, and spends the winter in the northern part of South America.

ROYAL TERN, *Thalasseus maximus*

This is the largest of the thirty-nine species of the STERNINAE. It is sharp-winged and more graceful than the gulls, LARINAE. The wings are sharp-pointed, the dagger-shaped bill is sealing-wax red, and the top of the head is black with a conspicuous crest. The Royal Tern is 53 cm (21 in) in length and breeds along the coasts of the southern United States, as well as the West Indies and West Africa. Terns do not soar like gulls, but fly along with steady wing beats, head and beak down, ready to dive vertically to pick up a fish. Terns have webbed feet, but their legs lack the muscles to propel them, so that they dive with a splash and emerge flapping with a fish in their beak and, with a few quick wing beats, they are again in the air.

BELTED KINGFISHER, *Megaceryle alcyon*

Grey-blue above, with an erected crest, this bird has a band of the same colour above the upper chest, and a rust-red band across the lower chest. This 33 cm (13 in) long bird breeds in temperate North America.

PURPLE MARTIN, *Progne subis*

In addition to the resident Galapagos Martin, three additional hirundines regularly visit the Galapagos. The male Purple Martin is a dark, metallic violet-purple in colour, but the female is dull with light creamy-buff underparts. It is well known in temperate North America as a colonial nester, often utilizing multiple nestboxes. The erection of the latter has been advocated as a means of controlling noxious insects.

BANK SWALLOW, *Riparia riparia*

This small hirundine is uniformly brown above and white beneath, with a brown band across the chest. The tail is only slightly forked. It is found in colonies practically throughout the Northern hemisphere, in fairly open country where it feeds over water. This is the Sandmartin of Britain. It excavates a tunnel in a sandy bank or cliff 60–90 cm (2–3 ft) in length with a chamber at the end in which the eggs are laid. North American birds winter in South America.

BARN SWALLOW, *Hirundo rustica*

Another hirundine found throughout the Northern hemisphere. The North American subspecies is, however, slightly smaller than the European. The upper parts are uniformly blue-black and the throat and forehead are chestnut-red. The outer tail feathers are elongated. This is the Swallow of Britain whose arrival, in spring, is a joyful event.

BOBOLINK, *Dolichonyx oryzivorous*

Breeding in the eastern parts of North America, this 20 cm (8 in) bird is a member of the exclusively New World ICTERIDAE. The male is black except for the nape and back which are buff, and the wing and tail feathers are edged with buff. It winters in Argentina.

CHAPTER 8

Reptiles

The visitor to the Galapagos will be impressed with the reptilean wealth. Two hundred years ago he would have been even more so, and most probably would have relied on reptile flesh for his sustenance for a year or more ahead. Today, the Giant Tortoises are not so much in evidence but the iguanas and Lava Lizards are still present in great numbers and the quiet observer, rowing around many of the mangrove-encircled lagoons, will often see dozens of turtles in the course of an hour.

Reptiles once dominated the earth, but, strangely, their numbers dwindled until, at the present time, it is only in tropical areas (that is in areas specially suited to cold-blooded animals) that reptiles persist in any numbers. In size they do not approach the dimensions of some of the enormous creatures of the past. It would seem that predation by mammals of greater intelligence has played the greater part in bringing this about.

Only four principal groups of reptiles are found alive today. These are the crocodiles and their relatives; the lizards and snakes; the tortoises and turtles, and, lastly, the strange little Tuatara from islands off New Zealand. They all share the character of possessing a scaly skin which gives them a great advantage over the amphibians in that they are able to conserve water. On the other hand, they differ from birds and mammals in that they are cold-blooded, and from mammals in that the jaws are furnished with teeth of a simple and undifferentiated type. (Mammals have teeth of several different sorts and of a constant pattern.)

Reptiles, then, show a transition between amphibia and mammals. On the Galapagos, amphibians are absent. Not only

could they not survive in marine conditions, but neither could they
survive in the arid zone around the edge of each island.

GIANT TORTOISE, *Geochelone elephantopus*

Species of Giant Tortoise were formerly distributed over a wide area
of the world, but today occur only on certain islands of the Galapagos and on Aldabra, an atoll in the Indian Ocean. Within recent
times Giant Tortoises were present in the Galapagos in extraordinary profusion, but, for reasons which will be apparent, they are
today much less common. A male Giant Tortoise may weigh as
much as 270 kg (600 lb) and be up to 1·5 m (6 ft) in length, so that
one can see why the islands were called Islas Galápagos (Tortoise
Islands) by the early Spanish visitors. The visitor today must spend
a long day ashore and tramp and climb several hot, dusty kilometres
before seeing a wild Giant Tortoise. Woodes Rogers, the British
buccaneer, likened the back of these huge reptiles to the top of an
old hackney coach, and one can imagine the raucous merriment of
these men as they climbed on top of the shiny, black carapace and
tried to ride!

Until recently tortoises were found on nine islands, though there
is some doubt about the existence of natural populations on Jervis
and Narborough. They are now also extinct on Charles and Barrington, and the Abingdon race is represented by one solitary male
which is now looked after by the Darwin Station, while the National
Park Service try to find him a mate! They are now present only on
Albemarle, Duncan, Indefatigable, Hood, Chatham and James.
(Virtually the whole population of Hood is now to be found at the
Darwin Station where they have had considerable success in breeding.)

The food of the Giant Tortoise consists of almost any sort of herbage. The leaves and fruits of bushes, grasses and algae, and, in
the arid areas, the pads of prickly pears make up their main diet. If
opportunity permits, however, they will eat a much wider variety of
food, even rotting goat carcases having been reported as being eaten.

They are fond of water and drink regularly, making long journeys
to pools and springs at high altitudes near the centres of the islands.
They also like to submerge in the pools and will construct wallows
of liquid mud allaying irritation caused by ticks and mosquitoes.
Well worn paths made by the tortoises converge on the pools and
springs and it was from these that the early Spanish visitors learned

Dome-shaped race of tortoise

of their location. Temperature regulation is said to take place by the tortoise moving from shaded to unshaded areas, but there is not the same rhythm of resting in the shade of bushes during midday as practised by the Giant Tortoise of Aldabra. The Galapagos tortoise, however, makes a 'form' in the herbage in the late afternoon and spends the night there.

The breeding season varies somewhat from island to island, but on Indefatigable is said to be from March to July. The males become aggressive, chasing smaller males, and go through mock battles with every male, charging each other and striking heads. The females are sought out and copulation takes place. The female then makes a journey to a traditional nesting site (after having taken a long drink to fill herself with water) which is usually in the lowlands where the soil is fine and dense.

The nest is made by the tortoise first urinating on the soil, then rotating with a hind leg in the softened patch. This forms a cavity up to 25 cm (10 in) deep and 17 cm (7 in) in diameter. She then lays 7–20 white, spherical eggs, about the size of billiard balls, in the egg-chamber. A cap is then made on top of the chamber with soil, sealed by the tortoise sliding about on top of it. When this dries, a hard lid is formed. The young hatch out from four to eight months later and appear to have little difficulty in scratching their way out of the chamber. One tortoise was observed to make five nests in half a day.

In many areas, eggs, and later the young hatchlings are heavily preyed upon, not so much by the endemic Galapagos Hawk, as by the feral domestic animals—cats, dogs, pigs, donkeys, goats and rats.

In captivity an individual has been known to reach an age of 150 years, whilst in the wild 100 years is probable.

The riddle of the origin of the Giant Tortoise in the Galapagos still remains to be solved. There were giant tortoises on the mainland of South America in Miocene times which is within the period when the Archipelago was formed, 10–15 million years ago. The most probable explanation is that the ancestral stock crossed from the mainland on a large vegetation raft, being brought thither by the currents which could move at the rate of 120 km (75 miles) per day.

Over the last three hundred years or so Man has been the greatest enemy of the Giant Tortoise. The early Spanish visitors, then the buccaneers, followed by the whalers, removed and consumed very large numbers. The log-books of only a small proportion of the US whaling fleet reveal that, during the nineteenth century, over a period of thirty-seven years more than 13,000 tortoises were taken. This was not only because the meat and oil were palatable, but the living tortoises could be stacked in the holds without food or water and would remain alive for over a year. Today very few are killed by man; indeed the Ecuadorian National Park Service, together with the Charles Darwin Station on Santa Cruz, are carrying out a large programme of rehabilitation of the subspecies most in need of help. In those islands where only small numbers remain, breeding programmes have been designed where the eggs are taken and hatched artificially, then the hatchlings are reared to such a stage that rats will not attack them. They are then liberated in the island of their origin. The tortoise populations of Duncan and Hood have already been augmented in this way.

There is an important relationship between the tortoises and the species of prickly pear present on the different islands. On the islands of Culpepper, Wenman, Bindloe and Tower, that is, those in the north of the Archipelago with the exception of Abingdon, the species of prickly pear, *Opuntia helleri*, is low-growing and the spines are soft and flexible. This species occurs nowhere else. In addition, on the island of North Seymour, there is another low-growing species, O. *zacana*. All these islands are now devoid of tortoises.

On the other hand, on all those islands which support tortoise populations, or where they have occurred in the past but are now extinct, the species of prickly pear (of which there are four) are large and tree-like with a branchless trunk. Such a growth-form in prickly pears occurs only in the Galapagos. It has been suggested that the tortoises produced the selection pressure resulting in the tree-like form.

All the different forms of the Giant Tortoise in the Galapagos are considered to belong to one species described as long ago as 1827 by Harlan. He named his specimen *Testudo elephantopus*, and it came from Charles where it is now extinct. Each of the larger islands has a distinct race or subspecies whilst there are five subspecies on Albemarle, each associated with a different volcano. Eibl-Eibesfeldt gives the subspecies of *Testudo* (now called *Geochelone elephantopus* as follows:

chathamensis, Chatham. Rare
hoodensis, Hood. Very rare

elephantopus, Charles. Extinct
porteri, Indefatigable. Numerous
ephippium, Duncan. Rare
wallacei, Jervis. Extinct, some doubt as to existence
darwini, James. Fairly numerous
abingdoni, Abingdon. Single surviving male
phantastica, Narborough. Probably extinct, some doubt as to existence
   becki, Albemarle. Fairly numerous
   microphyes, Albemarle. Fairly numerous
   vicina, Albemarle. Fairly numerous
   guntheri, Albemarle. Fairly numerous
   vandenburghi, Albemarle. Fairly numerous

One form possesses a long neck and long legs, whilst the carapace is narrow, at the same time turning upwards at the front and flared at the sides. This allows the neck to be stretched upwards without being much inconvenienced by the front rim of the carapace. Thornton describes the shape of the carapace as resembling a Spanish saddle, and it is known as the 'saddleback'. This form inhabits Narborough, Duncan, Abingdon, Albemarle (Volcan Wolf) and Hood and in general is to be found in arid areas where prickly pears are of the tree-form type. The long neck and legs not only enable the tortoise to make its way through much rougher terrain, but also enable it to reach the lower or hanging branches of the tree cacti. The young tortoises of whatever form are much alike, the saddleback character only developing as the animal gets older. This character is also usually more pronounced in the male.

There is variation, however, not only in the shape of the carapace, but in the length of the neck and limbs. There are also differences in size, in colour and in the thickness of the carapace. There are, however, two main types with many intermediates. The Vice-governor of the Galapagos told Charles Darwin that he could give the island of origin on seeing any tortoise from the Archipelago. He may have given the correct answer some of the times or even most of the times, but it would be improbable that he did so every time.

The short-necked forms, with dome-shaped carapace, are associated with abundant low vegetation, easily browsed or grazed from tortoise height. This is the form found on James, Indefatigable, Chatham, Southern Albemarle and Charles, although it is extinct in the latter island.

Saddle-shaped Race of Giant Tortoise, *Geochelone elephantopus*

Green Turtle, *Chelonia mydas*

GREEN TURTLE, Chelonia mydas

One species, the Green Turtle, is common around the shores and in a number of lagoons adjacent to sandy beaches. This species is distributed throughout the warmer oceans and, although much less frequent than formerly, due to its wholesale exploitation at egg-laying time, the visitor should have little difficulty in seeing them mating in the favoured lagoons. At this time the turtles will be seen swimming around the heads of the lagoons looking for mates. They are very wary, however, and quietness must prevail if they are to be observed.

The Green Turtle is so called on account of its green fat and it is this species which has been used for turtle soup. It is large, the shell reaching a length of 1 m (3 ft) or over, and such an animal may weigh as much as 270 kg (600 lb). This species may be identified by the possession of only four costal scutes on each side (these are the scutes lying between the mid-dorsal scutes and the marginal ones). In addition there is only a single pair of prefrontal scutes on the upper surface of the snout. The scutes of the shell do not overlap as do those of the Hawksbill Turtle, *Eretmochelys imbricata*.

The Green Turtle is said to feed mainly on eel-grass, *Zostera*, but many Pacific specimens are found to contain crustacea, molluscs and jelly-fish.

LAND IGUANA, Conolophus spp

Land Iguanas are found today on Indefatigable, Narborough, Albemarle, Seymour and Plazas. This is the species *Conolophus subcristatus*, and it was formerly found also on James and Baltra. On the latter island it was exterminated during the United States occupation in World War II. On Barrington, Land Iguanas occur also, but have been referred to a different species, *Conolophus pallidus*.

Land Iguanas of Galapagos are amongst the largest lizards in the world, being up to 1 m (3 ft) in length. They are stouter, heavier and usually larger than the Marine Iguana and are yellowish in colour, sometimes with patches of rusty-orange. The male attains the greater size. There is a row of spines along the back. The Barrington iguana is even more yellow in colour and the spines of the crest are larger. The Land Iguana appears slow and lethargic, but nevertheless can run at a good speed. They are exceptionally tame,

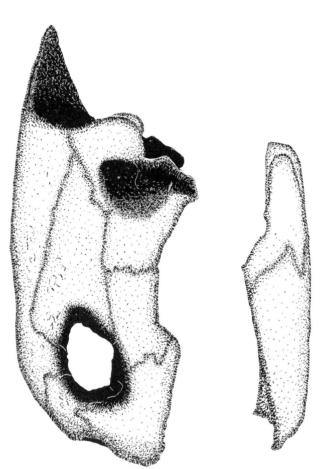

Skull of Green Turtle, *Chelonia mydas*

Land Iguana, *Conolophus subcristatus*

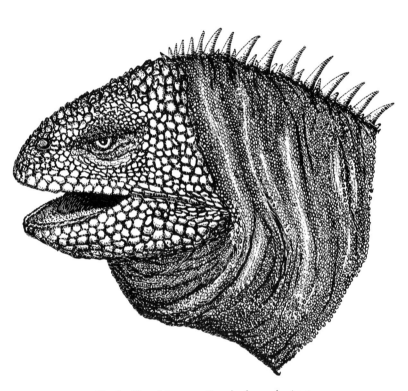

Head of Land Iguana, *Conolophus subcristatus*

allowing a very close approach before they languidly disappear into their burrows.

They live in colonies, excavating burrows in the shallow earth, with male and female usually inhabiting adjacent ones. At one time their burrows were so numerous that great difficulty was experienced in making a way across earth occupied by them. Darwin wrote of the difficulty experienced in finding sufficient room for a tent because of the burrows. They are herbivorous, but not exclusively so. Although their diet usually consists of buds, leaves, grasses and the fruits and pads of prickly pears, they have also been seen to take animal matter such as crabs and grasshoppers. They do not appear to experience any difficulty in consuming prickly pear, spines and all and will climb prickly pear to get at the pads.

On the islands where they occur, they appear to be distributed rather sporadically, as (although colonies are to be found in many coastal situations) Thornton records sighting them around the rim of the crater on Narborough.

During the breeding season the males take up territories and will fight intruders. They mainly rush and shove, but will also bite and hold on to each other's jaws.

In the past they have been hunted for their skins, but today their greatest enemies are rats and wild pigs which destroy their eggs.

They have recently suffered heavily from attacks by feral dogs on Indefatigable. Some of the survivors have been moved to the Darwin Station where a successful breeding programme has been started.

THE MARINE IGUANA, *Amblyrhynchus cristatus*

The Marine Iguana is found along all the rocky shores, sometimes in extraordinary numbers. In particularly favourable situations, such as shelving rocks or promonotories, the rocks may be obliterated by the tightly packed herds. They grow up to 90 cm (3 ft) in length. Generally they are sooty-black in colour, although some subspecies are suffused with green or red. The top of the head bears a number of blunt, whitish projections and the spines of the crest (especially of the males) are long and light-grey in colour. The snout is blunt and the sharp teeth are close to the surface, enabling the animal to chew seaweed off the rocks. This is its main food but they are known occasionally to eat marine animals. At least one herd lives in semi-domesticity on Indefatigable where they readily take raw fish and table scraps.

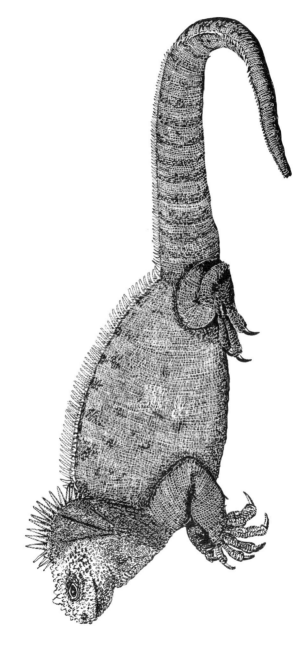

Marine Iguana, *Amblyrhynchus cristatus*

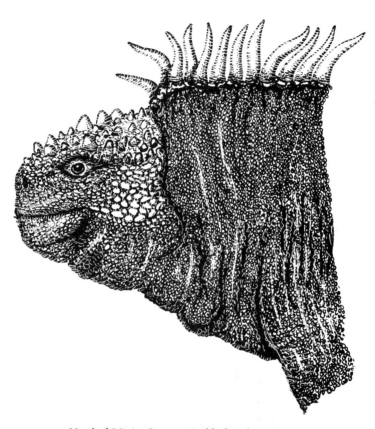

Head of Marine Iguana, *Amblyrhynchus cristatus*

This species is unique in being the only marine lizard searching for, and eating, its food under water. It is a good swimmer, although it does not use its legs for this, but presses them to its sides, progressing by alternate sideways sweeps of its laterally-compressed tail. It is sometimes seen swimming some distance from land, with its head well out of the water. The claws are long and strong and serve to hold on to rocks when subject to wave action. They can climb up vertical cliffs, as on Hood. In their feeding journeys, they are known to reach a depth of 10·5 m (35 ft) and to stay submerged for an hour. They drink seawater, but possess a mechanism for excreting excess salt. These are small 'salt' glands located between the eye and nostril beneath the skin, and they open into the nostrils. From time to time a jet of saline secretion is ejected from the nostils and this it does when disturbed.

The breeding season occurs during the hottest period of the year (January–February) when the male takes up a territory and assembles a group of females. There is a 'nodding' courtship and, after mating, the female repairs to a sandy beach where two large, white, soft-skinned eggs are laid in a shallow burrow. After an incubation of about two months the young hatchlings dig their way out. Predation takes place on a large scale when the iguana is young and, indeed, later in the year, their number appears small.

For all their long periods of submersion in seawater, they are infested by ticks, but two finches, *Geospiza difficilis* and *G. fuliginosa*, are often seen searching the iguanas and feeding on the ticks.

All marine iguanas are generally placed in one species, *Amblyrhynchus cristatus*. This is divided into a number of subspecies which have not been completely worked out. However, names have been given to the subspecies from Narborough, *A. c. cristatus*; from Duncan, *A. c. ater*; from Tower, *A. c. nanus*, and from Hood, *A. c. venustissimus*.

LAVA LIZARDS, *Tropidurus* spp

Small lizards are particularly abundant over most of the Galapagos and, as they are exceptionally tame, showing little fear of man, they seem to occupy almost every few square metres! They are known as Lava Lizards due to their habit of sitting in the scorching sun in open situations, especially on the very hot lava.

They have been classified into seven species as shown opposite.

Tropidurus grayii, Charles
T. bivittatus, Chatham
T. pacificus, Abingdon
T. habelii, Bindloe
T. delanonis, Hood
T. albemarlensis, Albemarle
T. duncanensis, Duncan

They are all less than 30 cm (12 in) in length and each species bears a characteristic, reticulated colour pattern. In most species the males are the larger, but the females may be identified by the dull, glowing red colour of the cheeks or throat region. During the breeding season both sexes hold territories, although that of the male is larger and may often include several female territories. Males are aggressive to males only, and females to females.

The male Lava Lizard is an ardent lover. He seizes the female by the leg, carries or drags her some distance, shifts his grip onto the back of her neck, then copulates with her. The female solicits such behaviour.

Geckos, GECKONIDAE

Geckos belong to the above family of lizards. They have a number of special characteristics by means of which they can be identified. They are small, only a few centimetres in length and the large eyes do not possess movable lids, so that they are always open. They are nocturnal, but during the daytime, when they are usually in hiding, the pupil is reduced to a thin, vertical slit. The tongue is fleshy and broad, slightly nicked at the end and capable of being protruded forwards. By this means it catches its insect prey. It loses its tail with consummate ease and then regenerates it again. This is a convenient sort of tail to have when it is grasped by a predator.

The skin of geckos is usually soft, but with little granular tubercles sometimes with small ossifications or calcifications. Perhaps one of the most characteristic features, however, concerns the feet, the digits of which are able to adhere to smooth surfaces. This is brought about by numerous transverse lamellae which spread out when pressure is put upon them, but, when the pressure is released, cause a series of small vacua. This feature gives the digits a dilated effect at the apex.

In addition to this, each lamella is fringed with minute hair-like

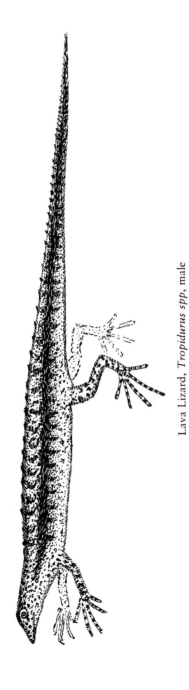

Lava Lizard, *Tropidurus spp*, male

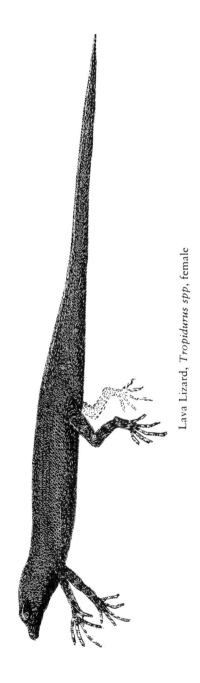

Lava Lizard, *Tropidurus spp*, female

excrescences which can catch even the slightest irregularity of the surface. Variations of this technique occur amongst the different genera but the general picture is the same.

Geckos produce a sound which, in some species, resembles the word 'gecko'. Males are generally larger than the females and the number of eggs laid is usually two.

The Galapagos geckos are classified into six species:

Phyllodactylus tuberculosis, Chatham
P. *gilberti*, Wenman
P. *leei*, Chatham
P. *barringtonensis*, Barrington
P. *galapagoensis*, Indefatigable, James and Albemarle
P. *bauri*, Charles and Hood

Five of these are endemic, but that found on Chatham also occurs widely on the mainland to the north and south. The genus has a wide distribution throughout the tropics and there is one European species.

Another widely distributed gecko, *Gonatodes collari*, has recently been introduced into Chatham.

SNAKES, *Dromicus* spp

Except on the northern islands, snakes are common. They belong to the above genus and have been variously classified as to species. One authority recognised seven species but the most recent classification gives three as follows, all of which are endemic:

D. *biserialis*, occurring as a separate subspecies on Charles, Hood and Chatham
D. *slevini*, occurring as two subspecies, one on Narborough, Albemarle and Duncan and the other on James, Jervis, Indefatigable, Baltra and Barrington
D. *dorsalis*, occurring as three subspecies, one on all the central islands, except Duncan, a second on Narborough and the third on Albemarle

The *Dromicus* snakes of the Galapagos grow up to about 1·20 m. (4 ft) in length and are very slender. They are dark brown in colour with either yellowish spots or marks along the back, or two yellowish-brown stripes. They are non-poisonous and feed mainly on Lava Lizards and grasshoppers, but will also take young Marine Iguanas.

Thornton considers that the distribution of the different forms of both snakes and Lava Lizards is evidence to show that the central islands at one time had a close connection, Duncan, however, excepted.

CHAPTER 9

Fish

There are 269 species of fish known from Galapagos waters. They belong to 88 families. Compared with that of other oceanic islands in the tropical eastern Pacific, this fauna is a rich one, although typical of the region. Three quarters of the total number of species consist of shore forms, whilst the remainder are pelagic or coastal pelagic. The 960 km (600 miles) of deep ocean separating the Archipelago from the American mainland appears just as much a barrier to those fish associated with the shore as it is for land-based animals. No fewer than 23 per cent of shore species of fish found in the Galapagos are endemic and most of these are so strongly differentiated from their congeners that difficulties arise in naming mainland species as probable ancestors. Of the 46 Galapagos endemic species, 34 show close relations with eastern tropical Pacific species, whilst 5 are related to forms characteristic of the Peruvian–Chilean warm temperate region.

Two endemic fish appear to be derived from Indo-West Pacific forms, and one is related to a West Atlantic species. The relationships of three species are questionable so were not included in this analysis which is due to Rosenblatt and Walker.

BLACK-FINNED REEF SHARK, Carcharhinus maculipinnis

Whereas the White-tipped Reef Shark reaches a length of about 2·5 m (9 ft), the Black-Finned Reef Shark is usually smaller. It is often present, however, in considerable numbers and Cousteau states that it is the only species which will take an immediate bite at prey and attack it without a thorough reconnaissance as practised by other species. Eibl-Eibesfeldt mentions seeing one 2·5 m (9 ft) long around the Guy Fawkes rocks. He was diving at the time and one performed

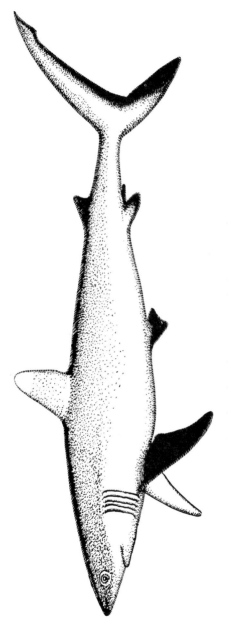

Black-finned Reef Shark, *Carcharhinus maculipinnis*

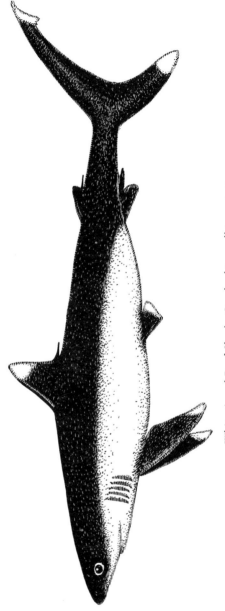

White-tipped Reef Shark, *Carcharhinus albimarginatus*

the head-shaking movement which this species makes preparatory to biting. This type of movement is thought to be the same as the one which the shark makes when it has already taken a bite of its prey, and has the effect of sawing a piece of flesh off the body. It is not a particularly reassuring sight!

WHITE-TIPPED REEF SHARK, *Carcharhinus albimarginatus*

The white-tipped fins and larger maximum size distinguish this shark from the black-finned species. It is potentially dangerous and often common. Sharks bear their young alive and a brood of about twenty is general. Dolphins are able to protect themselves against shark attack by driving them off, and, sometimes, killing them by swimming straight at the belly of the shark and thrusting their strong beaks into it.

HAMMERHEAD SHARK, *Sphyrna lewini*

This species is easily distinguished by the curious lateral projections at the front of the head, the eyes and nostrils being situated at the tip on each side. It reaches a length of about 4 m (14 ft), hunts in small groups or packs and is considered dangerous to man. Zuber records finding himself amongst three 3·5 m (12 ft) hammerheads resting on a sandy floor just off Hood Island. The strange adaptation of the head shape in this one shark species has no satisfactory explanation. It has been suggested that the wide spacing of the nostrils (they are close to the eyes) would aid food detection by smell.

GREAT WHITE SHARK, *Carcharodon carcharias*

The Great White Shark occurs in the open seas around the Galapagos. It reaches a length of about 11 m (36 ft) and is the shark most feared by divers, although Cousteau states that they always fled on sighting him.

WHALE SHARK, *Rhincodon typus*

The largest fish, it may reach a length of 20 m (65 ft) and a 9 m (30 ft) Whale Shark is common. It is a slow swimmer, achieving only about 3 knots and seldom surfaces, but follows ocean currents rich in animal life, such as the Humboldt. The mouth is always open and it swallows vast quantities of planktonic organisms, whilst large, bony plates allow it to crush anything too big to be swallowed

Hammerhead Shark, *Sphyrna lewini*

whole. The mouth may be up to 1·5 m (6 ft) in width and from 30–50 cm (12–20 in) in height.

The Whale Shark is not dangerous to man, certainly not from its mouth, although a too inquisitive diver might get a flick from its enormous tail. A side view gives it a hunchbacked appearance and the colour is grey-brown on the back with yellowish-white spots which are vaguely grouped as transverse bands. The belly is yellow or white.

BASKING SHARK, *Cetorhinus maximus*

This huge shark, second only to the Whale Shark in size, attaining a length of about 13·5 m (45 ft), is likewise harmless. It feeds on whatever organisms pass into its mouth, such as plankton and small crustacea and fish. It makes extensive migrations in search of feeding grounds. In tropical waters it seldom surfaces, yet it keeps near the surface when it follows the Gulf Stream off the west coast of Ireland and Scotland where its capture from time to time has been of importance to small communities as food, and the larger communities in respect of literature.

TIGER SHARK, *Galeocerdo arcticus*

This is a massive species, upwards of 6 m (20 ft) not being uncommon. It has faint lateral 'tiger stripes' and the mouth is disproportionately large, even for a large shark. It is dangerous.

GALAPAGOS SHARK, *Eulamia galapagoensis*

This reef shark is much like the White-tipped Reef Shark. It possesses a broad snout and grows to a length of about 2·5 m (8 ft). It is said to swarm in Galapagos waters.

SPUR DOG or PORT JACKSON SHARK, *Heterodontus quoyi*

This very small shark possesses a spine in front of each dorsal fin. It has a strange, bull-nosed appearance and is covered with irregular spots. The young are born in an egg-case surrounded by a spiral flange. One specimen of this shark was taken from the stomach of a Tiger Shark.

SPOTTED EAGLE-RAY, *Aetobatus narinari*

This ray, smaller than the Manta, is usually not more than about 1·5 m (5 ft) across. From its distinct spotted appearance it is sometimes called the Leopard Ray. The tail is proportionally longer than

Spotted Eagle-ray, *Aetobatus narinari*

that of Manta. It is often seen at the surface. This ray is remarkable for its pavement-like teeth by means of which it can crush large molluscs such as oysters and clams. A number of other species of ray are known but the one most commonly observed when bathing is the Sting-ray (DASYATIDAE) which usually keeps to a sandy bottom. It is easily seen, and a little splashing frightens it away.

The Sting-ray can cause a painful wound if the foot comes into contact with the serrated spine. This is due to the presence of special tissue located along either edge of the spine which secretes venom and which appears glistening white under the skin which covers the spine.

Rays do not possess dorsal fins and so lack a stability organ helping them to keep upright in the water. Although the large pelvic fins continuous with the head might be held to compensate for this, rays usually keep either to the bottom or the surface.

GIANT DEVIL-FISH or MANTA-RAY, *Manta birostris*

This huge, bat-shaped fish is often seen in Galapagos waters frequently close inshore where deep water occurs, such as around Daphne. It generally cruises close to the surface when it can be identified by the fins (wings) just breaking the surface together. It will sometimes jump clear from the water as much as 1·5 m (5 ft) and its large 4·5–6 m (15–20 ft) wide body, of 450 kg (1,000 lb) weight, creates a sound like a rifle shot. The large wing-like fins give great propelling force and boats have often been dragged considerable distances at great speed when the Manta has been harpooned. It is a feeder on small marine animals which are directed into its huge mouth by two fleshy protuberances. The young of the Manta are born alive and are of large size, being about 90 cm (3 ft) across and a tail length of about 2·5 m (8 ft). The rays are cartilaginous fishes, related to sharks.

PUFFERS or GLOBE-FISHES

These fishes have rounded bodies protected with spines and are heavily armoured. Consequently they cannot move very fast, but they possess a second and very curious line of defence. They can inflate their bodies by swallowing air or water, and if they possess spines or prickles these are firmly erected. They then float, generally upside down, impervious to predation except by old-time

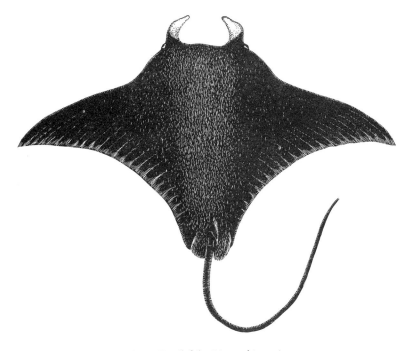

Giant Devil-fish, *Manta birostris*

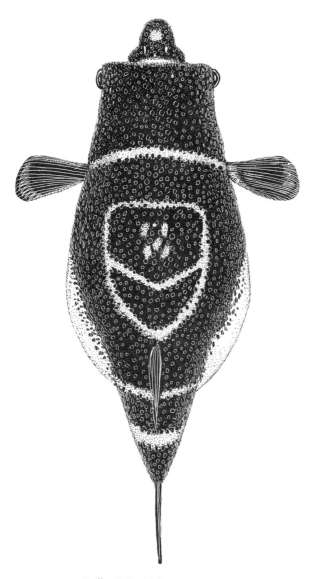

Puffer Fish, *Chilomyctenus* sp

Sun-fish, *Mola mola*

sailors who fished them out of the sea and dried them as souvenirs. The rigid body of these fish makes propulsion by sinuous body-movements impossible and, in fact, movement takes place by the dorsal and anal fins being fanned. Globe-fishes feed on molluscs and corals and their teeth are adapted to deal with such hard fare, being completely fused to form a pair of sharp, chisel-edged beaks.

The flesh of the globe-fishes is poisonous, although when specially prepared it is a delicacy in Japan where it is known as '*jugu*'.

SUN-FISHES

The sun-fishes of the family MOLIDAE are related to the porcupine and puffer-fishes (DIODONTIDAE and TETRAODONTIDAE) although very different from them in appearance. The warm seas of the world support three genera of these usually gigantic and strange fish. It is impossible from the deck of a ship in Galapagean waters to identify them, but when one observes a sharp, blade-like fin sticking out of the sea surface, oscillating slowly to and fro, the dorsal fin of a gigantic sun-fish is being observed. The Round-tailed sun-fish, *Mola mola*, which is the subject of the illustration, has a peculiar appearance. The body is truncated immediately behind the dorsal and anal fins and the tail fin is continuous with both latter fins. This ton weight and 2·5 m (8 ft) long plate-shaped fish appears to drift with the ocean currents and is well adapted to do this. It protects itself against predatory attacks by a 5 cm (2 in) thick layer of hard, gristly tissue beneath the skin, exceptionally tough, like leather.

The sun-fish has a small mouth, but the teeth are fused together to form a hard, bony beak; it feeds almost exclusively on jellyfish.

SURGEON-FISHES

Surgeon-fishes belong to the family TEUTHIDAE, one of the many families of Perch-like fish with spinous first rays of the dorsal fin. The body is laterally compressed and the head is large. They are characterized by the possession of body-scutes near the tail, each furnished with a spine. The latter are often retracted into a sheath, but can be unsheathed quickly and they prove to be an effective weapon when the tail is lashed about. Surgeon-fishes are able to make sounds by rubbing together spines on certain of the fins.

The surgeon-fish illustrated is *Prionurus laticlavius* which is 26 cm (10 in) in length and was collected from near the shore at Charles

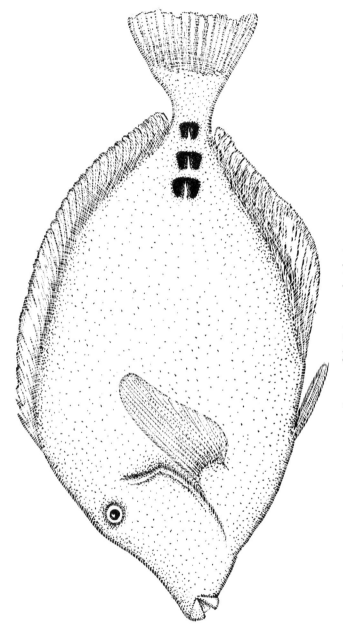

Surgeon-fish, *Prionurus laticlavius*

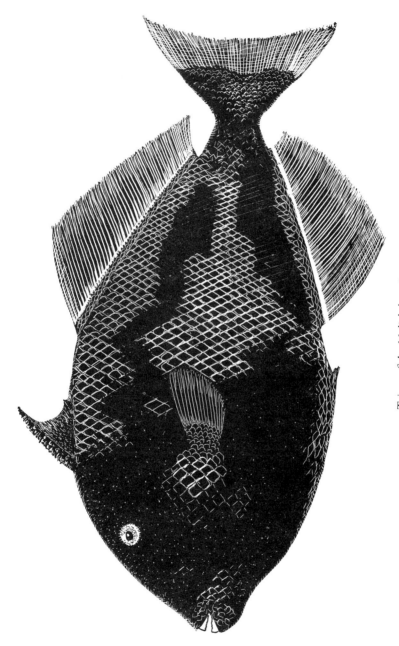

Trigger-fish, *Melichthys ringens*

Island. This species has a row of three spine-bearing scutes on each side.

TRIGGER-FISHES

These fish of the family BALISTIDAE are so named because of the strange mechanism to be found at the front of the dorsal fin. The first ray is a very stout spine but is grooved behind. At the base of the second ray there is a bony knob which fits into it. Thus, the first spine is immovable unless the second, acting as a trigger, is depressed. In most fishes there is an elaborate system of muscles which erect or depress the dorsal fin, as it is usually lowered when the fish is swimming at speed. In this case, however, the muscles actuate a protective device.

In trigger-fishes the pelvic fins are much reduced, often only visible as a single spine. The scales are usually more or less rhomboidal and very rough, often spiny and unlike most fishes, the teeth are firmly implanted into the bones of the jaw. The teeth are extremely strong and chisel-like and they are used to bore holes through the shells of molluscs in order to feed on them. Like the surgeon-fishes, trigger-fishes can 'stridulate', that is make sounds by friction, using their spines. The Galapagos species illustrated is entirely black to match the lava, although many trigger-fish are brightly coloured and this is thought to be of importance in warning off predators.

BUTTERFLY-FISHES

Butterfly-fish (CHAETODONTIDAE) are typical fish of coral reefs but some species are very common in the Galapagos lava tide pools, as well as the lava reefs. The body is almost plate-like but the fish is very agile and does not seem to mind showing itself.

The species, *Holacanthus passer*, is protected by spines on the gill-covers as well as three large spines in front of the dorsal and anal fins. It is mostly black with a yellowish-orange vertical bar on the tail and margins of anal and dorsal fins, a perfect camouflage if the fish wishes to hide in crevices in the lava.

PILOT-FISH, *Naucrates ductor*

The Pilot-fish occurs quite commonly, associating with, and swimming alongside, sharks and rays. It does not 'pilot' its associate towards its prey; indeed, it does not swim in front of the shark's mouth

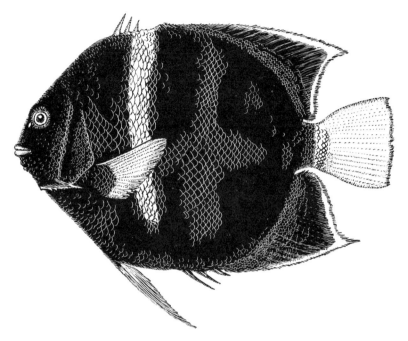

White-banded Angel fish, *Holacanthus passer*

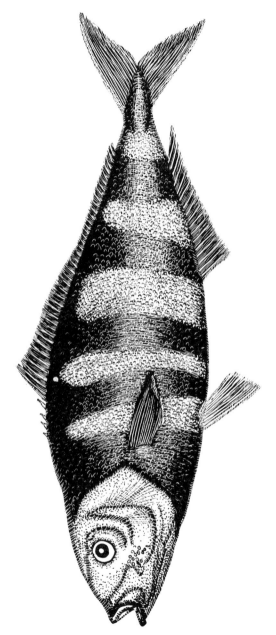

Pilot-fish, *Naucrates ductor*

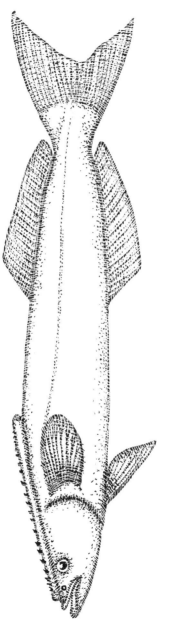

Side view of the Remora, *Echeneis naucrates*

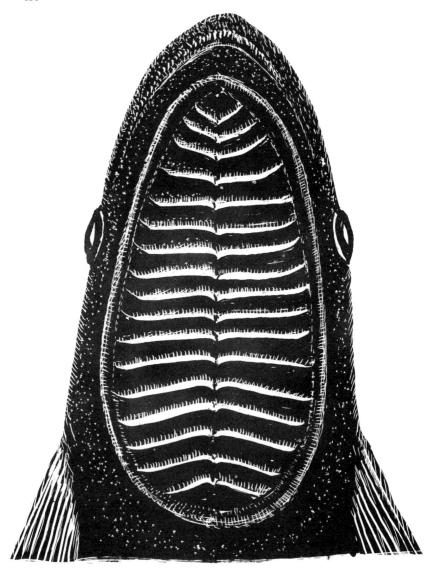

Suction disc of Remora, *Echeneis naucrates*

where it would risk being snapped up. However, it will swim almost in the mouth of a Manta-ray, knowing that it cannot harm it. It gains protection from its formidable companion of course, but what benefit is enjoyed by the shark or ray, is not clear. However, the Pilot-fish possesses a distinct pattern, the broad, transverse, dark stripes allowing the fish to be easily recognized. Underwater photographs of sharks with their Pilot-fish show this very well.

REMORA or SUCKING-FISH, Echeneis naucrates

The Remora possesses a large oval sucker above the head and pectoral fins. From the centre of the sucker a number of transverse ridges curve outwards, the hinder edges of which are movable. The outside rim of the sucker is membraneous. The sucker is a highly modified dorsal fin, the rays of which are divided and compressed sideways to form the ridges. The Remora attaches itself to any flat surface by moving into contact and then erecting the ridges. This produces a number of very powerful suctions pads making its removal extremely difficult by a direct pull. It can be removed, however, by sliding it forward or sideways. When attached, it assumes a moribund condition, becoming insensitive to rough treatment. No doubt this is an adaptation to allow more successful hanging on to its carrier when the latter is trying to remove it.

The keen observer will see the Remora being carried by dolphins and turtles and they are also carried by whales and sharks. The Remora gains protection by this device and an effortless method of transportation.

It gets its food from 'cleaning' sharks or other large fish. Parasites are removed by the specially adapted fine, but needle-sharp, teeth.

The Remoras are placed in the family ECHENEIDAE and appear greyish-white when viewed through the water. They are commonly seen in Galapagos waters.

BAT-FISH, Ogcocephalus darwini

The Bat-fish is surely one of the most bizarre of the Galapagos shore fishes. The body has an upper surface studded with spines and is flattened as it lives on the bottom, at least in the daytime—at night they are observed to rise to the sea surface. The pectoral fins are large and situated on arm-like extensions of the enlarged front end of the body. The pelvic fins and the anal fin are similar in appearance and size, and resemble small limbs with 'hands' at the extremities.

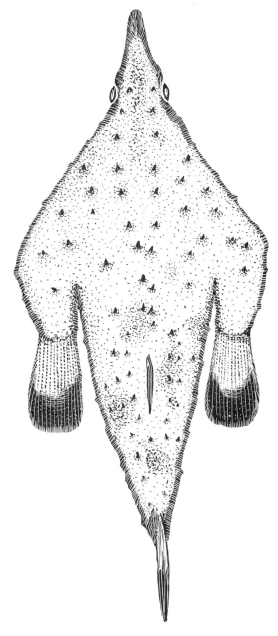

Bat-fish, *Ogcocephalus darwini*

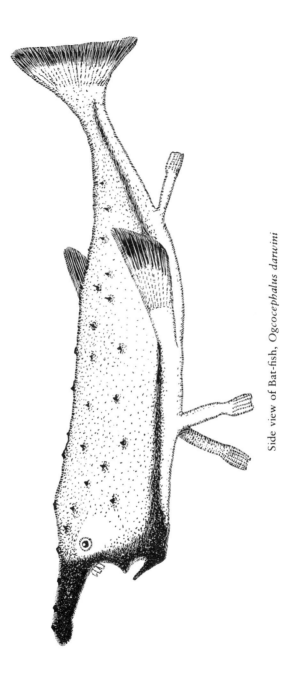

Side view of Bat-fish, *Ogcocephalus darwini*

These enable the fish to 'walk' along the sea bottom. There is a long curved snout and, in the angle made by it with the mouth, there is a group of whitish, soft-looking tubercles, bait for any unsuspecting small fish. If one comes to investigate it is eaten.

CHAPTER 10

Insects

It does not take long for an entomologist who has landed on a few islands of the Galapagos, to conclude that the number of insect species is small. With few exceptions the insects are small in size and dull in colour, facts which Charles Darwin noted himself during his visit in 1835.

ı As the Equator passes through the Archipelago, it might have been assumed that this faunal element would be in abundance, with many large, colourful species. Not much more than 960 km (600 miles) to the east on the same latitude, in Ecuadorian mainland, the large, brilliantly coloured, silvery-blue *Morpho* butterflies are common, but they are not to be found in the Galapagos. Linsley and Usinger (1966) compared the insect orders, families, genera and species found in the Galapagos, with those found in Britain. The comparison with Britain was convenient because it is one of the best-known faunas and because of the existence of the *Check List of British Insects* of Kloet and Hincks (1945).

In Britain there are three times as many families, ten times as many genera and thirty-two times as many species, as in the Galapagos.

Another aspect of the insect fauna is that it bears a resemblance to that of deserts. This is, however, to be expected when the wide, arid zone encircling the coastal area of the islands is studied. Except for insects of the mangrove areas, sometimes extensive in the Galapagos, immigrant insects would not only have to succeed in traversing several hundred kilometres of sea, but also must be capable of surviving in the semi-desert coastal areas.

In spite of the insect collections which have been made, beginning with Darwin in 1835, Linsley and Usinger were of the opinion that

141

many species await discovery and subsequent research endorses this.

Insect orders not on Galapagos

Let us consider which of the 28 orders of insects are not found, or rather, have not *yet* been found on the islands. Firstly, no species of the order PROTURA have yet been collected—yet in the British list of insects no fewer than 17 species in 4 genera are given. However, in comparing the speciation of insects of the Galapagos with that in Britain, it must be remembered that the latter is one of the most heavily collected areas in the world, inhabited by large numbers of collectors of many of the insect orders.

The isolation of the Galapagos, together with the presence of an arid, almost desert-like belt around the islands, makes systematic collecting a difficult task which can only be undertaken by scientific expeditions. The small numbers of the islands' inhabitants can only help in a limited way.

Stoneflies, PLECOPTERA, are absent. The immature stages of this group are aquatic and almost always found in fast-running, well oxygenated fresh water. The adults are weak fliers and are seldom found far from the margins of streams and lakes. It is not, therefore, surprising that they have not been found in the Archipelago.

Stick and leaf insects, PHASMIDA, are absent. About 2,000 species are known, seldom found outside the tropics, and the largest number of species occur in the oriental regions. They are mainly leaf-eaters. A number do not possess wings and move only very slowly. They are not aggressive colonizers, yet two species originating from New Zealand have recently become established in the Scilly Isles as members of the British fauna.

The silk-weavers, EMBIOPTERA, are absent. Although they possess only weak flight, their species have made their way to a number of isolated areas, Ascension Island for example. The 140 species in this order are found in almost all areas of the tropics and extend to the southern temperate regions also.

Mayflies, EPHEMEROPTERA, are absent. Several features of the biology of these insects render the colonization of remote oceanic islands improbable. The immature stages are passed in fresh water and the adults are weak fliers. The duration of adult life is short, in many species being only a few hours. A sub-imaginal stage usually takes place. This is a winged stage unique in insects, in which a skin must be shed before the final reproductive stage is assumed. The hazards of predation are met by a 'saturation' emergence in which very large numbers take to the wing within a few hours.

Caddis flies, TRICHOPTERA, are absent. This is another insect order where the immature stages are passed in fresh water. A number of species fly relatively strongly and a number of cases have been noted where they have been found far from fresh water. The larvae, however, require oxygenated water, or moving water, so that the arid and coastal zone would have to be negotiated before caddis flies could be established in the islands.

Thrips, THYSANOPTERA, have only recently been recorded. This is not surprising as these minute insects are often introduced with imported plants.

Scorpion flies, MECOPTERA, are absent. This is a small order of about 300 species, most of which spend the immature stages in soil and moss.

Again fleas, SIPHONAPTERA, have only recently been recorded. This is remarkable as with so many feral cats and dogs their associated flea fauna must be abundant—to say nothing of the Human flea, *Pulex irritans*!

PRIMITIVELY WINGLESS INSECTS, APTERYGOTA

The primitive orders of insects are very poorly represented in the Galapagos. These insects require damp, sheltered situations and no doubt the arid coastal region has prevented colonization. There are two species only of spring-tails, COLLEMBOLA, each confined to a single island. There are also recorded two species of bristle-tails, THYSANURA, but these are more generally distributed. Finally, one member of the DIPLURA is confined to Indefatigable.

DRAGONFLIES, ODONATA

Six species of dragonfly are recorded from the Galapagos, and some of these are common and may be seen resting on the mangroves or hawking for insects over the lagoons. Only one species of the less robust ZYGOPTERA, is included. Members of this suborder are easily identified by the stalk-like base of the wings and the vertical position of the wings when at rest. The immature stages of all dragonflies are aquatic, occurring exclusively in fresh water so that it would be of great interest to learn where this takes place in the coastal areas. Dragonflies fly strongly and are known to spend some of the adult stage away from the breeding areas, but, nevertheless, the adult would require an accurate memory, or a guiding mechanism, in order to locate the small areas of fresh water for egg-laying.

Some species of dragonfly are known to migrate and it is conceivable that the species arrived in the Galapagos by their own flight.

GRASSHOPPERS, LOCUSTS AND CRICKETS, ORTHOPTERA

The order ORTHOPTERA is represented by twenty-one species of which eight are in the family ACRIDIDAE, comprising the short-horned grasshoppers and locusts. Some of the species are present in large numbers and the visitor to the islands will certainly be aware of them, perhaps more especially in the more arid situations. In contrast to the great majority of the insects of the Galapagos which are small and dull-coloured, a number of the short-horned grass-hoppers are brightly coloured, orange-red, green and black being the most common colours. Their flying jumps often land them on black lava where the Lava Lizards abound, and to which they fall prey. However, a number also desiccate if they do not move off fast enough from the blistering heat of the bare lava. They are found in life-like positions, as though just about to jump, but in a completely dried-up condition.

In this family there is a considerable amount of subspeciation. *Sphingonotus tetranesiotis* is found as 4 subspecies, each on a different island.

The species *Sphingonotus trinesiotis* is also found in 3 subspecies on different islands. The well known genus of locusts, *Schistocerca*, is represented by 3 species of which one, *literosa*, is found as 3 sub-species on different islands; another, *melanocera*, is found as 5 subspecies, also on different islands.

The remaining acridid genus, *Halmenus*, consists of two wingless species, *eschatus*, only from Wenman Island and *robustus* which occurs as 3 subspecies. One of these is found on Charles, one on Albemarle, and one on Indefatigable and James.

The long-horned grasshoppers, TETTIGONIIDAE, are also relatively numerous. About 4,000 species are known from the tropical areas of the world and 9 are known from the Galapagos. However, in contrast to the acridids there is practically no subspeciation. There are 9 species in four genera. *Liparoscelis cooksoni* is recorded from

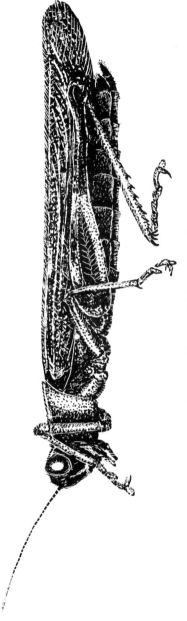

Medium-sized locust, *Schistocerca melanocera*

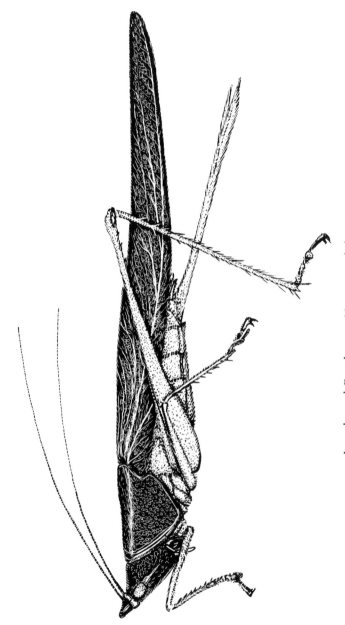

Long-horned Grasshopper, *Neoconocephalus triops*

Long-horned Grasshopper, *Liparoscelis cooksoni*

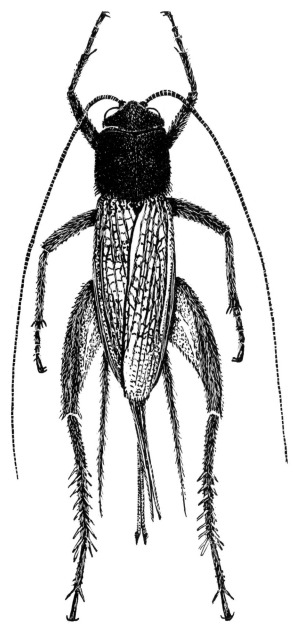

Widely-distributed cricket, *Gryllus assimilis*

Floreana and Isabela and a subspecies is recorded from Indefatigable and Hood.

Of the crickets in the family GRYLLIDAE there are 4 species in 3 genera with no subspeciation. *Hygronemobius speculi* is the only species confined to one island (Albemarle).

COCKROACHES, DICTYOPTERA: suborder BLATTARIA

The cockroach order DICTYOPTERA, is of special interest in that a number of cosmopolitan, undesirable insects could have been transported to the Galapagos through shipping. Nine species in seven genera have been recorded, but of these, four are common pests of buildings associated with man, not only in the Central American region, but also in many other parts of the world, tropical, subtropical and, indeed, in many temperate areas. These are *Blattella germanica*, *Periplaneta americana*, *P. australasiae*, and *P. brunnea*. The last three species are all found in Chatham, whilst *P. americana* and *P. australasiae* are found additionally in Charles. Strangely, *Blattella germanica*, perhaps the most cosmopolitan of the above-mentioned species, is recorded only from uninhabited Hood, but the most widespread of all cockroaches, *Blatta orientalis*, is not recorded from the Galapagos!

PRAYING MANTIDS, DICTYOPTERA: suborder MANTODEA

The MANTODEA provides one species. This is *Galapagia solitaria*, recorded from Albemarle, Charles and N. Seymour. It is interesting to speculate on the fragility of the establishment of an exclusively predacious species, obviously intensely related to the numbers of the excess populations of phytophagous species over a period of many years.

EARWIGS, DERMAPTERA

These insects possess rounded hindwings which fold neatly under the small modified forewings (tegmina), and horny, claw-like forceps at the end of the abdomen. Many species, however, are apterous. Two only of the 900 or so world species have been recorded in Galapagos, both in the family FORFICULIDAE, to which belongs the common earwig of Europe (established also in the United States of America), *Forficula auricularia*. The species found in the Galapagos are *Anisolabis bormansi* on Chatham and *Euborellia annulipes* on Chatham and Albemarle.

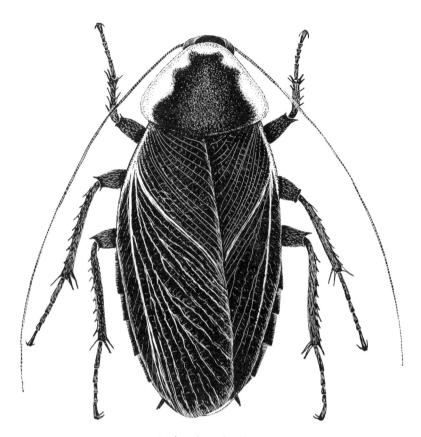

Medium-sized cockroach, *Phaetalia pallida*

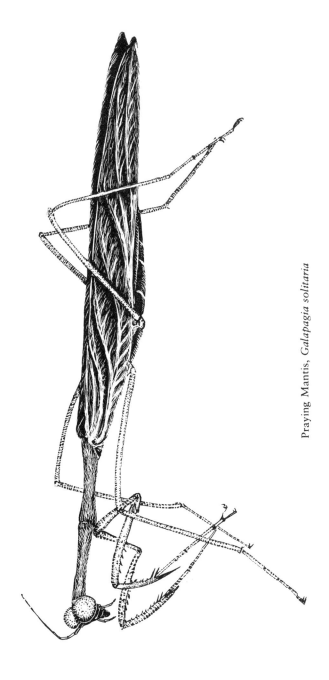

Praying Mantis, *Galapagia solitaria*

151

TERMITES, ISOPTERA

Only 6 species of termites are known from the Galapagos and 5 of these are classified in the family KALOTERMITIDAE. These are generally known as the drywood termites on account of the special nature of their biology. Colonies of drywood termites occur in timber, either dead branches of trees or in converted timber, without connection with sources of moisture in the ground or, indeed, any external water source. They are usually found in coastal areas or islands.

It is of some significance that in the KALOTERMITIDAE the position of the worker caste is anomalous in that all members of the colony are probably capable of development to the adult stage. It would appear that the KALOTERMITIDAE are much more likely to be transported, either with or without the aid of Man or his commerce. This seems to have been borne out by this family recorded from the Galapagos. There are many modern records of various species of drywood termite colonies occurring on ships.

Of the three members of the genus *Incisitermes*, *galapagoensis* has been recorded from Wenman and Tower. It is apparently not found elsewhere. The species *pacificus* has been found on Narborough, James, South Seymour, and Albemarle, and is found nowhere outside the Galapagos. *Incisitermes immigrans*, on the other hand, is not only widespread in the Galapagos, but is common in the Hawaiian Islands, Ecuador and Peru. In the last two countries it is a pest of building timbers.

Cryptotermes darwini is listed as occurring in James, Indefatigable, Gardner and Charles, but it is thought that this is, in fact, *Cryptotermes brevis*. This latter species causes significant damage to wooden buildings in coastal areas, including Florida, the West Indies, Colombia, Brazil, Peru, Chile, West Africa, East Africa and South Africa, but its presence in the Pacific are the isolated instances of Hong Kong and Galapagos. *Cryptotermes fatulus* is recorded from Albemarle and James islands and elsewhere it is recorded only from west Mexico and islands nearby.

The remaining Galapagos termite is *Heterotermes convexinotatus*, in the family RHINOTERMITIDAE. These are known as subterranean termites and are found in large, highly differentiated colonies underground, where access to moisture is available.

Heterotermes convexinotatus is distributed on the American

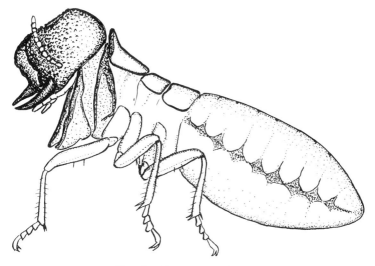

Termite, *Cryptotermes brevis*

mainland in Panama, Mexico and Costa Rica. It is also found in the West Indies and in the Galapagos it is recorded from Indefatigable, where there is an extensive settlement at Academy Bay.

BIRD LICE, PHTHIRAPTERA: suborder MALLOPHAGA

It is not surprising that with the large and varied bird population of the Galapagos, there is an equally varied bird lice fauna. Sixty-one species of the MALLOPHAGA in twenty-five genera have been recorded. This is, of course, the one order of insects where the method of transportation to the Archipelago is certain! They were carried at the base of the feathers of birds that have reached the islands.

No species of MALLOPHAGA possesses wings and all are external parasites of birds, although a substantial number are found on mammals. A number of species are well known as infesting domestic animals, eg *Trichodectes canis* on the dog; *Felecola subrostratus* on the cat, and *Bovicola bovis* on cattle. None of these is listed by Linsley and Usinger, but it is difficult to believe that they are absent in view of the large number of feral animals living on the islands.

SUCKING LICE, PHTHIRAPTERA: suborder ANOPLURA

These insects are bloodsucking ectoparasites of mammals exclusively. In all 225 have been described and man is the host of two, and his domestic animals to another dozen. Only two species are recorded from the Galapagos. With so many feral animals and man himself, often living under conditions where hygiene standards are low, this small number of species is surprising.

BOOKLICE, PSOCOPTERA

PSOCOPTERA or booklice are small, or very small, insects of which about a thousand species have been described. They have long thread-like antennae of up to about fifty segments. Wings, which are delicate, membraneous and often bearing a dark pattern, are generally present, but many species possess only rudimentary wings either in both sexes, or in the female only. PSOCOPTERA, sometimes referred to as psocids, occur amongst a variety of vegetable organisms on fragments of which they feed.

No psocids were listed by Linsley and Usinger, although three species were identified in general collections by Lee and Thornton

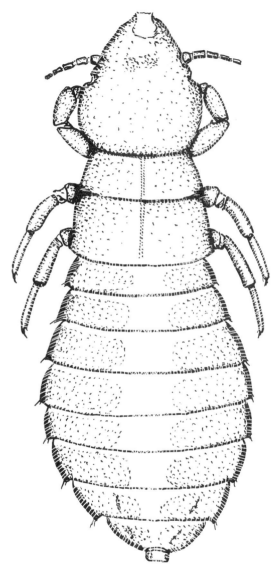

Bird Louse, *Pectinopygus nannopteri*

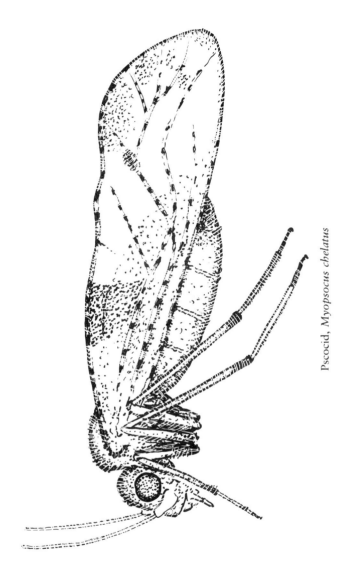

Pscocid, *Myopsocus chelatus*

(1967). However, Thornton spent six months in the Galapagos when all sixteen islands were visited. He collected 39 species of which 20 were new and confined to the Galapagos. The 39 species are contained in 22 genera compared with the British 68 species contained in 35 genera.

Plant bugs etc, HEMIPTERA

In this order of insects, two pairs of wings are usually present of which the anterior pair are of a more horny consistency than the posterior pair, either uniformly so (HOMOPTERA) or with the apical portion more membraneous than the remainder (HETEROPTERA). The mouthparts are adapted for piercing and sucking. It has been stated that no other order of insects is so directly concerned with man's welfare, on account of the injury to vegetation causing loss and destruction to his crops. Many act as vectors, transferring the causative viruses of many plants' diseases. The effect of this is often multiplied by the extraordinary rate of reproduction in a number of species.

If the HOMOPTERA section is excluded, 14 families containing 41 species are recorded from Galapagos. In the HOMOPTERA there are 3 families containing another 38 species.

There are 6 shield-bugs, PENTATOMIDAE, of the known 3,500 species, and 6 coreids, COREIDAE, of the known 2,000 species. Both these families are very well represented in South America and almost all species are plant feeders. Of the lygaeid bugs, LYGAEIDAE, there are 4 species. One lace-bug, TINGIDAE, is present and the bed-bug, *Cimex lectularius*, is recorded in one locality. The largest family of the HETEROPTERA group is the MIRIDAE, there being about 5,000 species and, of these, 13 occur in the Galapagos.

One of the most remarkable of insect genera is *Halobates*. Its species are almost unique in spending their lives on the ocean surface, not having any connection with land, nor with fresh water. This genus belongs to the GERRIDAE whose members are predominantly associated with fresh water as the familiar 'water-skaters'. They are small with long spidery legs, no wings and the abdomen is very small. The under-surface is covered with a dense pile of short hair which acts as a hydrofuge. In this way the *Halobates* remain on the surface of the sea and never get wet! Their eggs are laid in rafts, usually attached to floating debris.

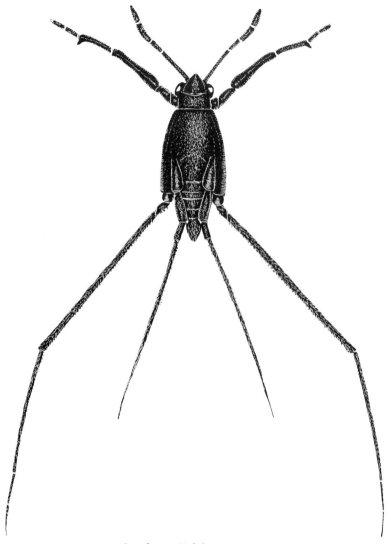

Sea-skater, *Halobates micans*

Larvae and adults feed on dead marine animals floating on the surface.

Three species are recorded from Galapagos waters, of which *H. robustus* appears to be endemic. It is recorded from Indefatigable, Charles and Albemarle and, no doubt, is more generally distributed, being at the mercy of the ocean's currents.

Halobates sobrinus and *H. micans* are recorded as having been found near the Galapagos.

Butterflies and Moths, LEPIDOPTERA

The visitor to a new country will often assess the richness of insect life by the numbers of butterflies seen. It is the large-winged, colour-
ful insect species which catch the eye of even the casual observer. The Galapagos, however, are poor in their numbers of species of this attractive group of insects. Eight butterflies have been recorded hitherto, although this chapter will add another to the list. The paucity of the butterfly fauna can be gauged by comparison with that of the British Isles where there are eight times as many; and while of moths there are eighty-nine in the tropical Galapagos, but well over 2,000 in temperate Britain. Many butterflies and moths fly strongly and continuously, and, with the prevailing winds westwards from South America's shores, one might have expected more lepidopterous colonization. In this case (an order of mostly exclu-
sively plant-eating insects), the family of plants, and sometimes a particular species of plant, needs to be firmly established first.

Amongst the many anomalies of faunal distribution in the Gala-
pagos is the absence of any species in the PAPILIONIDAE, a family of large, showy butterflies distributed throughout the world, reaching their greatest abundance in the tropics.

GALAPAGOS SULPHUR BUTTERFLY,
Phoebis sennae marcellina

This is the most conspicuous butterfly in the Galapagos. The male measures up to about 6 cm (2 in) across the outstretched wings, whilst the female is generally a little smaller. The upper side of the wings of the male is a bright sulphur-yellow and the underside is yellow with a slight reddish-brown tinge with a few small reddish-
brown speckles. The female has the upper side much less bright

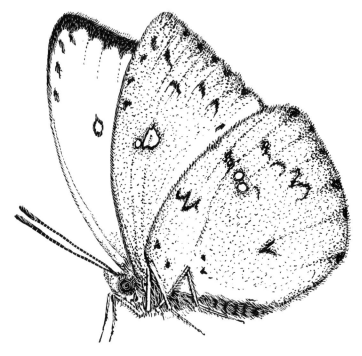

Galapagos Sulphur Butterfly, *Phoebis sennae marcellina*, female

Galapagos Fritillary, *Agraulis vanillae galapagensis*

and there is a brown margin to all wings. There is a small circular spot in the middle of the forewings and a few zig-zag marks. The underside of the female is yellow, densely speckled with orange, with a few wavy marks of a light reddish-brown colour and in the centre of each wing are a couple of tiny silvery spots, edged with the same colour. The antennae only gradually thicken towards the tips.

It is widely distributed throughout the islands and is the sole member of the important family PIERIDAE.

GALAPAGOS FRITILLARY, *Agraulis vanillae galapagensis*

Three species of butterfly in the family NYMPHALIDAE are recorded from the Galapagos, two being members of the genus *Vanessa*, and one of the genus *Agraulis*. This is our present species, *A. vanillae*, subspecies *galapagensis*, the Galapagos Fritillary. It is medium-sized, about 5 cm (2 in) across the outstretched wings. The top side is a fulvous orange, streaked and marked with black, typical of many fritillary butterflies. On the underside, the hindwings bear a number of large silver spots edged with black, with some smaller ones along the hind margin. The apex of the forewings, too, is similarly splotched with silver. This is the same species, but not sub-species, as the Gulf Fritillary of the southern United States.

VIRGINIAN CYNTHIA BUTTERFLY, *Cynthia virginiensis*

The only two Galapagos butterflies which could possibly be mis-taken for each other are species in the genus *Cynthia*, previously classified in the genus *Vanessa*. British naturalists will know them as Painted Ladies. They are virtually indistinguishable by the in-expert from the top surface alone. This is fulvous orange, spotted and marked with black, with a few white spots on the almost black tips to the forewings. On the underside, however, the Virginian Cynthia has two large eye-like marks in the brown background area. To the outer side of the eyes is a lavender-coloured band and to the inside of the brown area is a delicate lace-like pattern extending to the body. The underside of the forewings is suffused with rosy-pink at the base, with a much smaller area of lavender at the tip. However, if a Painted Lady is seen flying on Albemarle then it is almost certain to be the Virginian Cynthia as this is the only Gala-pagos island from which it has so far been recorded.

FOUR-SPOTTED CYNTHIA BUTTERFLY, *Cynthia carye*

This butterfly has, so far, only been recorded in the Galapagos from Chatham. Although the upper surfaces of the wings are similar to the foregoing species, it is readily distinguishable if a near approach can be made when the insect is resting, or sucking nectar from a flower. There will be seen four bluish spots on the underside and the lavender band is absent. On the forewings the suffusion is light orange—not rosy-pink. It measures about 5 cm (2 in) across the outstretched wings.

MONARCH BUTTERFLY, *Danaus plexippus*

This is the largest Galapagos butterfly, being about 10 cm (4 in) across the outstretched wings. It was thought to be the only member of the DANAIDAE present in the Galapagos until recently, when it was discovered that *Danaus gilippus* was present on Albemarle. The Monarch is also known as the Wanderer in the United States, because of its long migratory flights. It often reaches Britain, but whether by flight or by means of an 'assisted' passage is not known. The Monarch has reached many Pacific islands this century, yet, so far, it has only colonized Chatham. This is the most populated island and visited by more trading ships, so that the possibility of the Monarchs having been introduced in this way seems likely.

The Monarch is easily identified from the other danaid, the Queen, by the veins of all wings, upper and undersides, being heavily marked in black. The Queen, on the other hand, has only the veins of the underside of the hindwings so marked.

QUEEN BUTTERFLY, *Danaus gilippus*

This is a medium-sized, reddish-brown butterfly already described with the Monarch. It occurs on Albemarle although overlooked by Linsley and Usinger. Specimens are in the British Museum collections.

GALAPAGOS BLUE BUTTERFLY, *Leptotes parrhasioides*

This minute butterfly appears to be common and widespread throughout the Galapagos. It is so small and its wings are moved so rapidly that it appears more like a tiny mass of grey-blue haze moving about the herbage. It is extremely alert and does not allow a near approach. It is the only member of the LYCAENIDAE, the blues,

The Virginian Cynthia Butterfly, *Cynthia virginiensis*

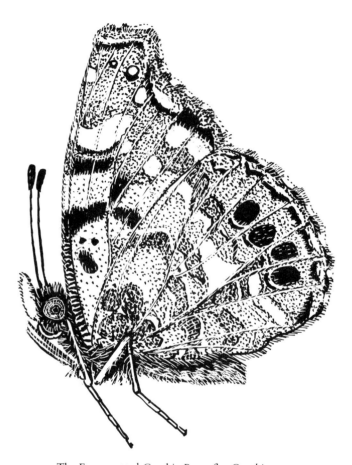

The Four-spotted Cynthia Butterfly, *Cynthia carye*

Monarch Butterfly, *Danaus plexippus*

Queen Butterfly, *Danaus gilippus*

Galapagos Blue Butterfly, *Leptotes parrhasioides*

hairstreaks and coppers, found so far in the Galapagos, so it can be identified with ease. The male is more or less uniformly bright, shining blue. In the female the blue patches are much restricted and there is a variable amount of lighter spotting. Along the base of the hindwings there are three or so black spots. The underside of both sexes is similar. The ground colour is grey on which there is a white wavy reticulation. At the base of the hindwing are five black spots edged with a brilliant, greenish-metallic colour.

Skippers, HESPERIDAE

Two species of skippers—that is species in the family HESPERIDAE—appear in Linsley and Usinger's *Insects of Galapagos* with the remark that an error in labelling has been suggested by Duzee. Presumably these two butterflies are not to be found in the Galapagos. Galapagos-taken specimens are absent from the insect drawers of the British Museum but it is a difficult task to prove the non-existence of a labelled specimen. Therefore we treat the following two species as though present until it can be proved that they do no occur.

THE MOURNING SKIPPER, *Erynnis funeralis*

This butterfly is of uniform, dark chocolate-brown colour with a few faint markings in a lighter brown, but with a long white fringe to the hindwings. It is now placed in the genus *Zarucco*. It measures 3.5 cm (1 in) across the outstretched wings.

Erynnis funeralis is recorded from Chatham.

THE LARGE-TAILED SKIPPER, *Urbanus dorantes galapagoensis*

This brown butterfly bears a number of rectangular or crescent-shaped yellowish spots on the forewings. The hindwings are devoid of markings, but large blunt tails are present. It is a well known species in Central and South America, but the Galapagos representatives are distinct.

THE BLUE-SPLASHED SKIPPER, *Heteroptia bryaxis imalena*

This is one of the most beautiful of the skipper butterflies usually notable for their dull coloration but swift and erratic flight. The wing area, compared with the size of the body, is small relative to other butterflies. The apex of the antenna is produced in a strongly

Large-tailed Skipper Butterfly, *Urbanus dorantes galapagensis*

recurved hook—*see also Urbanus dorantes.* The thorax and abdomen of *Heteropia bryaxis* are especially stout. The wings are of a deep, dark chocolate-brown with the forewings splashed with luminescent, light silvery-blue. The long hairs on the base of the hindwings also have a silvery-blue sheen. All wings have a white fringe and the hindwings bear a pair of blunt tail-like projections. It is recorded from Albemarle. Its presence in the Galapagos, however, has been questioned.

HAWK MOTHS, Sphingidae

The family SPHINGIDAE is fairly well represented in the Galapagos, twelve species being listed by Hayes. These are the well known hawk moths. They are medium to very large in size and throughout the world there are something like 1,000 species, mostly concentrated in tropical and subtropical regions. One species, *Hyles lineata*, is cosmopolitan and is represented by the subspecies *florilega* in the Galapagos. Hawk moths are characterized by their elongated forewings with oblique outer margins. The antennae possess a small recurved hook at the extremity. Generally, but not invariably, the proboscis is of extreme length which allows nectar to be sucked from flowers with long tube or bell-shaped corollas. The streamlined body and the angulated wings give an impression of swift flight which is the case, but they can hover on fast-moving wings with precision whilst the proboscis searches for nectar in a flower. Nine of the twelve Galapagos species are represented by subspecies.

The Carmine Hawk Moth, *Agrius cingulatus*, is one of the largest Galapagean moths, measuring nearly 10 cm (4 in) across the outstretched wings. The forewings are mottled and banded in dark grey and dark brown on a light grey background, but the base of the hindwings and the banding of the abdomen is flushed with carmine. It is well distributed in the Galapagos, having been recorded from Chatham, Albemarle, Indefatigable, Baltra and Charles.

Manduca rustica galapagensis, is 9 cm (3½ in) across the outstretched wings. The forewings bear a number of transverse rippled bands in light creamy- and dark brown, and there is a prominent, dark, creamy-brown spot in the centre. The hindwings are much darker in colour and the bases are covered with long silvery-grey and creamy hairs. It has been recorded from Charles, Chatham, Hood and Indefatigable.

Hawk Moth, *Hyles lineata florilega*

Carmine Hawk Moth, *Agrius cingulatus*

Hawk Moth, *Manduca rustica galapagensis*

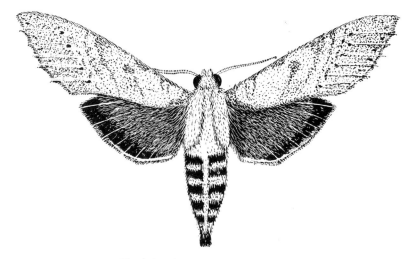

Hawk Moth, *Erinnys ello encantada*

Erinnus ello encantada is not quite 7 cm (3 in) across the out-stretched wings. The narrow forewings are light dove-grey with faint spots and markings in dark grey. The hindwings, however, are rich fiery-copper with a broad black edge. It has been recorded from Indefatigable, Charles, Chatham and Albemarle.

Arctiidae

Only four species of this family, which consists of the moths popularly known as tigers, ermines and footmen, are found in the Galapagos. Yet over 3,500 species have been described from the whole world and even though they reach their maximum numbers in tropical areas, forty species are known from Britain. Arctiid moths are generally characterized by being conspicuously coloured in red and yellow spots and bands. Many species, if disturbed by a predator, display these colours as a warning of their unpalatability.

The four Galapagean species belong to the footmen group. *Utetheisa galapagensis* is thought to be endemic and is recorded from Albemarle, Indefatigable, James, Charles and Baltra. *Utetheisa ornatrix* on the other hand is neotropical. The thorax is white with black spots. The wings are white with a pale carmine tinge and edged with bright orange-red spots, and with some black spotting. The underside of the wings, however, is a bright orange-carmine. This is displayed when the insect falls to the ground. The wings are folded over each other. This species is recorded from Albemarle and South Seymour only.

In Britain there is a related species the Crimson Speckled Footman, but the Mediterranean race, which sometimes finds its way to Britain, has the whole of the forewings covered with black and orange-carmine. Two other species have recently been described (Hayes 1975); *U. perryi* from James and *U. devriesi* from Abingdon.

Noctuidae

Hayes lists 72 species of moths in the family NOCTUIDAE as occurring in the Galapagos. Contrasting with this, only thirteen species of GEOMETRIDAE are recorded. The NOCTUIDAE is the largest family in the order LEPIDOPTERA. Over 3,500 species have been recorded from North America alone. The moths are dull and sombre-coloured, relying on their cryptic coloration in order to escape detection by

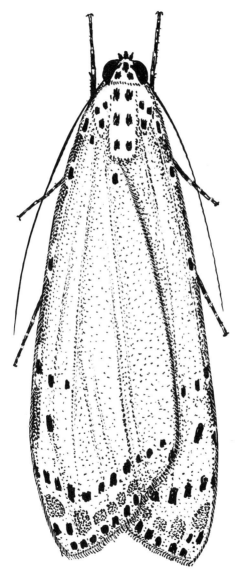

Crimson Speckled Footman Moth, *Utetheisa ornatrix*

Noctuid Moth, *Melipotis indomita*

Noctuid Moth, *Melipotis harrisoni*

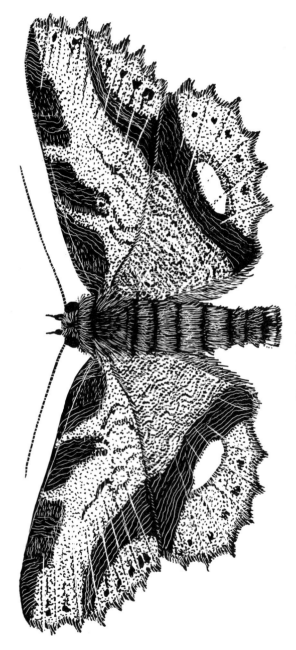

Noctuid Moth, *Zale obsita*

predators during daytime when they are resting on tree trunks, stones and other objects.

Two closely related species are illustrated. These are *Melipotis harrisoni* and *indomita*. Both are fairly well distributed, being found in Indefatigable, Albemarle and South Seymour, and whilst the former is recorded from James in addition, the latter is recorded from Charles. *M. indomita* is rather larger and more vivid than *M. harrisoni* and the transverse bar and oval mark are bright cream in colour with the general background of the forewings in a velvety-black. *M. harrisoni* has the transverse bar dull dopper in colour and the general background is dull and greyish.

Zale obsita is a noctuid moth rather more strongly coloured than most noctuids. Linsley and Usinger list a species of *Zale* without name, merely assigning it to the '*viridans* group'. This present species was taken by R. Perry and Tj de Vries on Indefatigable, and identified by A. H. Hayes. The background is pale straw in colour, but superimposed upon it is an intricate and delicate pattern of greys, browns, and reddish-browns, mostly in series of wavy bands. The darker coloration appears along the front edge of the forewings and a loop around the hind angle of the forewings, which continues as a broad band across the hindwings. This rather suggests that the insect rests with its wings spread out on the bark of a light-coloured tree. This is a large moth measuring 6 cm ($2\frac{1}{2}$ in) across the outstretched wings.

Geometridae

The GEOMETRIDAE is a large group of moths poorly represented in the Galapagos. Only 13 (Rudge 1973) species are recorded out of a world tally of over 12,000. They are slender bodied and fragile. In some genera the wings of the females are very much reduced so that they are flightless. The larvae are long and thin and there is usually a reduction in the number of abdominal 'false legs'. Often the larvae resemble twigs.

The geometrid moth *Oxydia (Sericoserna) lignata* is about 3·8 cm ($1\frac{1}{2}$ in) across the outstretched wings. It is a most variable species. From the small number of specimens examined it would appear that there is a sexual difference in the shape of the apex of the forewing. In the female it terminates in an acute point, but in the male it is obtuse. The range of variation is shown in the illustration.

This species is recorded from Chatham.

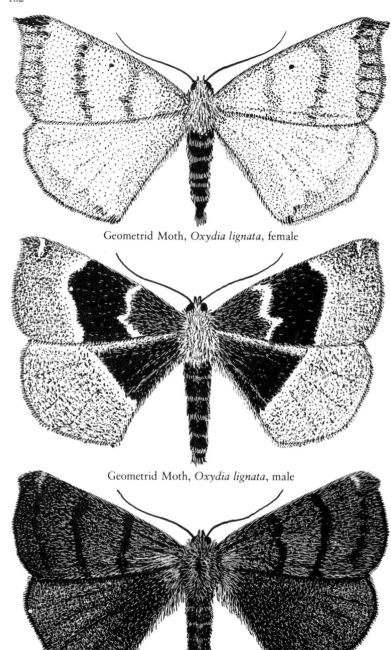

Geometrid Moth, *Oxydia lignata*, female

Geometrid Moth, *Oxydia lignata*, male

Geometrid Moth, *Oxydia lignata*, male

Beetles, COLEOPTERA

When Charles Darwin wrote of his visit to the Galapagos Islands in 1835, he remarked on the small size, dull colours and paucity of species of the insects. He wrote: '... excepting Tierra del Fuego, I never saw ... so poor a country'. Darwin thought that the insect fauna showed resemblances to that of a desert. Referring to the COLEOPTERA, Linsley and Usinger list 192 species contained in 107 genera and 39 families. If this is compared with the well known beetle fauna of the British Isles, we find that 3,729 species contained in 967 genera and 96 families are listed. Although in the British Isles the total number of species of all insects is some thirty-two times greater than the number found in the Galapagos, yet in beetle species the corresponding comparison is only fourteen times. One could assume that this group have been more successful in establishing themselves in the Galapagos than have insects in general.

Two species of tiger beetle, CICINDELIDAE, have been recorded. *Cicindela galapagoensis* seems to be fairly common around Banks Bay, Albemarle, as F. X. Williams collected a series of twenty-six in April 1906, all of them at night. It has also been collected from Clipperton Island.

It is about 1·2 cm ($\frac{1}{2}$ in) in length. The eyes are bulbous, black and very prominent, the prothorax is narrower than the head and dark in colour, whilst the wing-cases have a greasy-coppery look edged with yellow and with four yellow marks extending inwards. The legs are long and thin as is the case in this fast-running predaceous group.

The CARABIDAE, the other terrestrial, predominantly predaceous, beetle family, is relatively well represented in the Galapagos. There are 24 species known, contained in 7 genera. They are rather flattened with long, strong legs and thread-like antennae. In colour they are black or very dark, frequently with metallic lustre of various colours.

The specimen illustrated, *Calasoma galapageium*, bears the distinction of being the first beetle described from the Galapagos. It was collected by Charles Darwin in 1835 and the description of it was published in 1837. Darwin collected 29 beetle species from the Galapagos during his voyage on the *Beagle*, and the present species was collected almost certainly from the interior of James Island where Darwin spent a week.

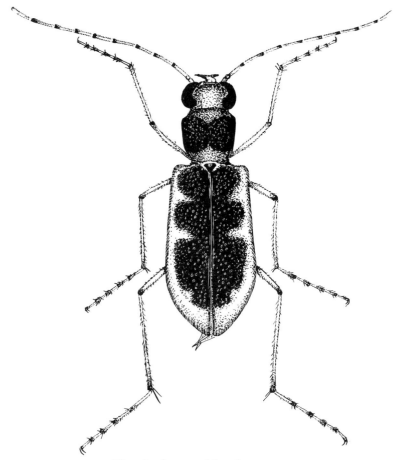

Tiger Beetle, *Cicindela galapagoensis*

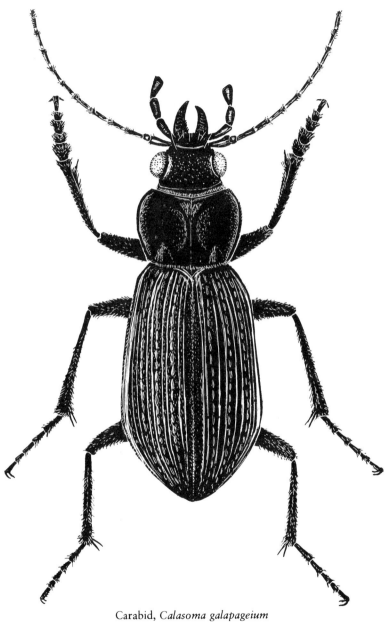

Carabid, *Calasoma galapageium*

Calasoma galapageium is black and shiny but with a greeny-blue lustre particuarly in the pit-like depressions on each side of the prothorax, and along the edges of the wing-cases. The wings, however, are abortive as they also are in two other species in this genus in the Galapagos, although *Calasoma howardi* is fully winged.

A number of water beetles in the families DYTISCIDAE (4 species), HYDROPHILIDAE (5 species) and GYRINIDAE (one species) are able to pass their immature stages in brackish water in the Galapagos. One hydrophilid indeed possesses larve found in putrid cacti. The widespread and large water beetle *Eretes stricticus* has a powerful flight and is found in a large number of isolated islands.

The family OEDEMERIDAE is of special interest on account of species being found on most tropical islands. In the Galapagos five species have been recorded. They are thought to breed in the driftwood washed up along the shores. The American and European species *Nacerdes melanura* is common and found in the bilges of wooden-hulled ships and has obviously been distributed in this way. It is possible that the Galapagos species arrived in the Archipelago by this means.

One species of oil beetle (MELOIDAE), *Cissites maculata*, has been recorded from Chatham. It parasitizes the larvae of the Carpenter Bee, *Xylocopa*. Fourteen species of ELATERIDAE have been recorded. This family is a large one, about 7,000 species being known from the whole world. On the whole they are dull-coloured insects but with the strange power of jumping into the air if they are laid on their backs. The noise they make with the pro- and mesothorax, as the trigger mechanism is released, gives them the name in England of Click Beetles.

However, the fireflies of the neotropical region also belong to the ELATERIDAE. Eggs and larvae of *Pyrophorus noctilucus* are luminous and light is emitted in the adult from the sides of the thorax and also the ventral surface of the abdomen. The larvae of this group are root feeders.

The family BUPRESTIDAE contains more than 15,000 species and many large genera, *Agrilus* comprising 700 species and *Chrysobothrus* 300. The larvae are wood-borers, a large number making flattened galleries just beneath or in the bark. One would, therefore, expect a rather larger number of species to have been recorded in the Archipelago if colonization has taken place by means of rafts of branches and vegetation. The adult beetles are fast flyers so that they would be able to traverse the coastal arid zone with ease. In fact, only three species have so far been recorded and all are apparently endemic. It is noteworthy that all are small or very small and two of the species are only 2 mm (·07 in) in length.

The larvae of BUPRESTIDAE, which are characterized by their much enlarged prothorax, would form part of the Woodpecker Finch's quarry.

Five species of ladybird beetles, COCCINELLIDAE, are recorded from the Galapagos, two of which, Cyclopeda sanquinea and Olla abdominalis, are widely distributed on the mainland of North and Central America and on many islands. The remaining species, Scymnus galapagoensis, Adalia galapagoensis and Psyllobora bisigma, are endemic. When in the bridge-house of the Golden Cachalot, about half a kilometre from Albemarle Island, a specimen of Cyclopeda sanquinea flew in through the open window!

The family TENEBRIONIDAE, with more than 10,000 species, is one of the largest in the COLEOPTERA. They are usually dark in colour and many resemble carabids. Tenebrio molitor and T. obscura are cosmopolitan pests of meal and flour, and the cylindrical, short-legged larvae are known as mealworms. Many species are able to live under desert conditions, a characteristic which would help in colonization. There are 43 species recorded from the Galapagos, apparently one of the most successful beetle families.

Two genera, Stomion and Pedonoeces, are endemic, with 18 species in the latter and 9 in the former; in addition there are 13 species in the genus Ammophorus.

A subspecies of Stomion galapagoensis, named punctipennis, has been described from Hood Island and two subspecies of Ammophorus galapagoensis, both from Wreck Bay and Chatham Island, have been described.

The longhorn beetles (CERAMBYCIDAE) are relatively well represented in the Galapagos; 18 species have been recorded. One would have expected more species of this family with exclusively wood-boring larvae, if the establishment of species has occurred through transport by drifting vegetation. Drifting tree branches and trunks would contain many cerambycid larvae. However, when such detritus gets washed ashore and the larvae produce adult beetles, they must be able to find the correct tree species for egg-laying. Although many cerambycids are able to complete their life cycle in

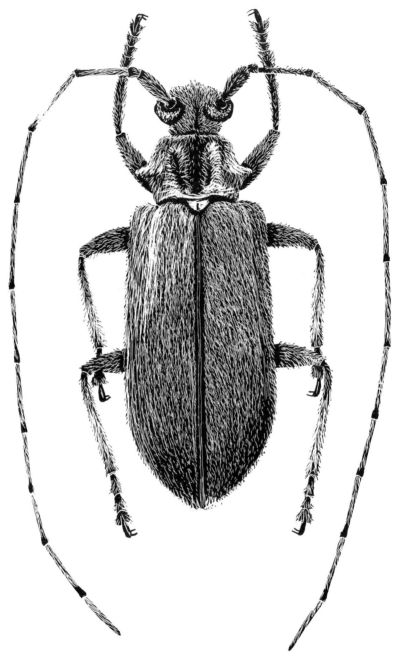

Cerambycid Beetle, *Estola galapagoensis*

a range of tree species, many require a specific tree. A few trees are found in the desert-like shore regions, but most occur at an altitude a kilometre or more from the shore.

The Galapagos cerambycid fauna is distinct from, although related to, species found on the South American continent and none attains the large size found in a number of species. The largest is just over 2·5 cm (1 in) in length, but most are about 1·2 cm ($\frac{1}{2}$ in) in length—not including the antennae.

The larvae of the cerambycids must play a large part in the activities of the two finch species that use tools in the shape of spines for their extraction from the tree trunks and branches. There is, however, an apparent anomaly in that photographs of the finches using spines as tools show them as needling the food out of flight holes. This is not where the larvae would be found! The well known oval flight hole is made by the adult beetle as it bores its way out of the wood at the end of its life cycle. The finch certainly could not find the larvae by looking, or poking its spine, into old flight holes. However, a large number of small round flaps were found by the author, some of which communicated with cerambycid tunnels under the thin bark. It appears that the finch pecks out the small flap and then looks in. If a larva is sighted then a spine is quickly found and the larva extracted. In the cases where the flaps were found the bark was very thin and it seems probable that the finch is able to detect the presence of the tunnels by the softness, or perhaps the elasticity, of the bark. This method of hunting for wood-boring larvae is confined to the Galapagos. Woodpeckers with their extremely long and spiny tongues are absent, but two species of finch have learnt, at some stage of their evolution in the Galapagos, the use of a tool. This is all the more remarkable when one realizes that this is of comparatively recent origin.

Leptostylus galapagonensis is not much more than 0·6 cm ($\frac{1}{4}$ in) in length and, although the background colour is reddish, it is covered with whitish scale-like hairs, except for the pattern of pit-like depressions and grooves. This gives a chalky appearance. The antennae are long and slender, much longer than the body length. The legs appear quite stout.

It has been found on Albemarle, James and Jervis islands. This little longhorn beetle could easily be overlooked.

Of the other families possessing wood-boring larvae, there are

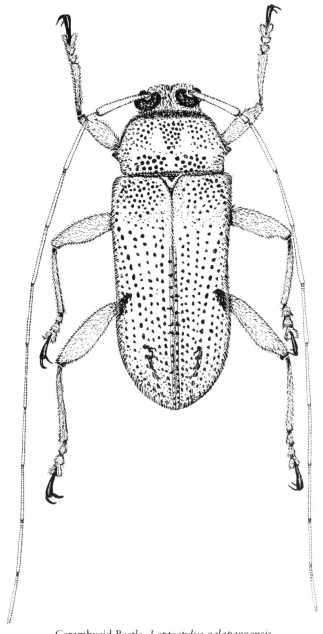

Cerambycid Beetle, *Leptostylus galapagoensis*

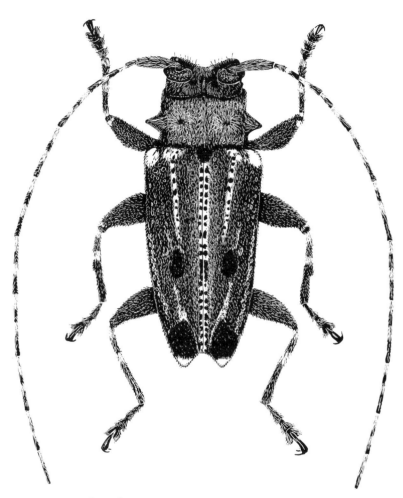

Cerambycid Beetle, *Acanthoderes galapagoensis*

Dark-coloured Weevil, *Gersteckeria galapagoensis*

four species of ANOBIIDAE recorded from Galapagos and three of BOSTRYCHIDAE, but no LYCTIDAE.

Only sixteen species of weevil (beetles of the family CURCULION-IDAE) have so far been recorded from the Galapagos. Very many species, however, are small and may easily remain undetected. On the other hand, it is the most numerous group of beetles, more than 35,000 species having been described. As they are associated with almost every kind of vegetable material, one would expect a much larger number of species to be found on the Galapagos.

Curculionid beetles are easily identified by the long, forward extension of the head, the rostrum, and by their possession of elbowed (geniculate) and clubbed antennae.

Gersteckeria galapagoensis is a cactus-eater and a member of a genus found in the more arid regions of the southern United States, Mexico and the West Indies. The immature stages would be readily transportable in cactus pads and three subspecies from Barrington Island, Hood Island and South Seymour have been described.

It is a robust-looking weevil with a strongly downwards- and backwards-curved rostrum, about 0·6 cm ($\frac{1}{4}$ in) in length. Dark brown in colour, with a creamish colour pattern due to a clothing of scales, no member of the genus possesses functional wings.

The two families PLATYPODIDAE and SCOLYTIDAE are sometimes included with the CURCULIONIDAE, and are of interest in their association with timber. Although of worldwide distribution, one species only in each family has been recorded from the Galapagos. *Platypus santacruzensis* is one species. The scolytid *Pycnarthrum isulare* is quite common and breeds in mangrove seeds.

ANTS, BEES, WASPS, HYMENOPTERA

Twenty-one species of ant (family FORMICIDAE) are known from the Galapagos. In this family of the HYMENOPTERA, however, two remarkably plastic species occur, both in the genus *Camponotus*. The species *C. macolentus* occurs in fourteen named subspecific forms, but these are not entirely confined to separate islands. The subspecies *duncanensis* is found both on Duncan and Charles, and *sapphirinus* on Indefatigable and South Seymour, whilst on Charles alone four separate subspecies are to be found.

Species of *Camponotus* are known as carpenter ants on account of their habit of excavating galleries in wood. They could, therefore, easily have been transported in floating forest debris. Certain species have been carried around the world in commercial timber, packing cases etc, but the degree of differentiation to be found in the Galapagos species precludes such modern forms of transport.

On the other hand, Wheeler, the great ant authority who had studied the ants of the Galapagos, remarked that doryline ants were absent, although they were of importance on the near mainland of South America. Dorylines are known as the driver ants. They construct no permanent nests but use temporary nesting places between periods of column marching. One cannot think of them being carried across 960 km (600 miles) of ocean unprotected.

The bees and wasps of the Galapagos are extraordinarily sparse in species. In the true wasps, family VESPIDAE, there is but one species, *Odynerus galapagensis*. Wasps of this genus are predaceous on lepidopterous larvae, or larvae of leaf-eating beetles or saw-flies. They are stung into immobility and stored in a cell in which the egg is laid. The latter is suspended from the roof of the cell by a filament and when the cell is closed the wasp takes no further interest in its brood. The relative scarcity of lepidopterous larvae on the Galapagos probably accounts for the lack of vespids.

Again, there is but one species of pompilid wasps, family POMPILIDAE. This is *Aporinellus galapagensis*. Pompilid wasps are characterized by their great agility. They are predaceous on spiders and usually lay their eggs in burrows in the ground. Some pompilids reach a length of 7·5 cm (3 in) and are amongst the largest of the HYMENOPTERA.

Two sphecid wasps are recorded, *Nitela darwini* and *Tachysphex galapagensis*. The former is recorded only from Charles whilst the latter is recorded from Albemarle and South Seymour only. All sphecids are solitary and lay their eggs on prey which has been stung into immobility. A wide variety of insects and spiders serve as hosts which remain fresh for several weeks after being stung. Parental care is rare in this family.

All visitors will see the blue-black bee, *Xylocopa darwini* (family APIDAE). This is the only species in the family recorded from the Archipelago. It is a solitary bee, although classified in a family with such familiar insects as the social honey bees. Strangely, the latter are absent from the Galapagos but nearly so are the brightly coloured, attractive flowers secreting nectar.

Species in the genus *Xylocopa* make their nests of larval cells in galleries bored into timber or in the hollow stems of plants. For the former reason they often do considerable damage to wooden structures in many parts of the world and are known as carpenter bees. *Xylocopa* is found on Albemarle, James, Duncan, Indefatigable, Baltra, Chatham, Charles and Gardner. It is often the first insect seen by the visitor to the Galapagos arriving in Baltra as it occurs in the small bay near the dock. The females are blue-black whilst the males are yellow, and they appear to be particularly attracted to yellow flowers.

Thornton states that if Indefatigable were part of an equivalent area of the mainland, about 100 species of solitary bees would be expected to be present, and yet *Xylocopa darwini* is a relative newcomer to the island. The bee requires nectar for its own nourishment and nectar and pollen for its larvae. Yet the nectar-producing plants with a sufficiently short corolla, to enable the bee to get at the nectar, are not in adequate supply. Nevertheless, the bee has found a way of slitting the base of long corolla flowers in order to get at the nectar which the long-tongued hawk moths would otherwise suck.

Two-winged or true flies, DIPTERA

The true flies are characterized by the possession of only a single pair of membraneous wings. The hind pair are modified as small knob-shaped organs known as halteres. The mouthparts are adapted for sucking and sometimes, in addition, as in the bloodsucking species, for piercing. The larvae are legless. This order is one of the largest, containing over 80,000 species. 6,000 species are known in the British Isles, but only 102 from the Galapagos. However, the latter are included in 27 families, while the British species are classified in 87 families. The British dipterous fauna then is sixty times more numerous in species but only three times more numerous in families.

Amongst those families in the less-developed suborder NEMATOCERA the number of species is rather small. There are five midges and four crane-flies. Of rather more than academic interest, however, the presence of the mosquito, *Aedes taeniorhyncus*, of ill-repute, is recorded as being present on Tower, Albemarle, James, Jervis, Indefatigable, South Seymour, Chatham and Charles. There is one biting midge (CERATOPOGONIDAE), *Forcipomyia fuliginosa*, recorded from Albemarle, South Seymour, Indefatigable and Gardner.

In the BRACHYCERA group of families there is one horse fly, TABANIDAE, this is *Tabanus vittiger*, recorded on Albemarle, Indefatigable, Chatham and Charles. The females are well known bloodsuckers and cause unrest amongst horses and cattle, their presence being advertised by their loud hum. There are three species of bee flies, BOMBYLIIDAE. The larvae of this family are parasitic, usually on other insects, so that we have to look to the Galapagos insect fauna for their hosts. These are most likely to be amongst the locusts and the carpenter bee, *Xylocopa*. There is a single robber fly, ASILIDAE, which is predacious, seizing insect prey with its strong, spiny legs. It is probable that a toxin is injected into the prey from a bite, as the captured insect usually appears moribund after the mandibles of the asilid have bitten into the body of the prey.

Ten species in the DOLICHOPODIDAE are present. These are small, bristly, metallic-looking flies, almost all of which are predacious, and often frequent the seashore where they feed on very small insects; but *Aphyrosylus setosus* almost certainly feeds on the wood-boring larvae of longhorn beetles (CERAMBYCIDAE). It is found on Charles.

In the CYCLORRHAPHA group there are five species of hover fly, SYRPHIDAE. These are medium to large in size and often brightly coloured, mimicking, stinging HYMENOPTERA. There are five vinegar flies, DROSOPHILIDAE. In the MUSCIDAE there are eight species including the house flies, *Musca domestica* and *Fannia canicularis*, and the biting *Stomoxys calcitrans*. There are three species of CALLIPHORIDAE and nine in the SARCOPHAGIDAE. The latter mostly breed in decaying animal and vegetable matter, although a few are parasites, principally of insects.

Finally, in the HIPPOBOSCIDAE there are seven species. These are ectoparasites of birds and mammals, and in many the wings are absent. The head is inserted into the thorax and strong claws are present to enable the insect to crawl through feather and fur. One species, *Olfersia fossulata*, is found only on Wolf Island and Daphne Major.

In the order NEUROPTERA there are two ant-lions, MYRMELEONIDAE, three green lacewings, CHRYSOPIDAE, and one brown lacewing, HEMEROBIIDAE.

CHAPTER 11

Other Invertebrates

Marine Invertebrates

What a colossal task to deal adequately with the enormous inverte-
brate fauna of the shallow water around the Galapagos! We can
only hope to point out a few of the more abundant or interesting
species with a brief description of each of the three main groups—
the CRUSTACEA, which includes the crabs, shrimps, and barnacles;
the MOLLUSCA, including the bivalve and univalve shells, and the
ECHINODERMATA or starfishes, sunstars, brittle stars, sea-cucumbers
and their relations. All these major groups are invertebrates, that
is, animals without backbones.

   We also include the terrestrial spiders and centipedes, having dealt
with the insects in a separate chapter.

Echinodermata—Starfishes, Sea Urchins and their Allies

This 'spiny-skinned' main group of exclusively marine animals has
little relationships with any other group. The noticeable difference
is that whilst most other animals have a form based on bilateral
symmetry, the echinoderms possess a symmetry based on five or
more radiating arms. The starfish is familiar to all, with its bizarre
appearance, its ability to develop arms to replace any which have
been cut off and the way in which it can walk in any direction. It
faces no particular direction when moving.

   The group is well represented in the Galapagos. The Many-
armed Sunstar, *Heliaster cunningii*, is particularly abundant on lava
rock, sometimes almost covering the entire surface. It is dull purplish-
black covered with small, creamy- orange-tipped spines. Its dark

Many-armed Sunstar, *Heliaster cunningii*

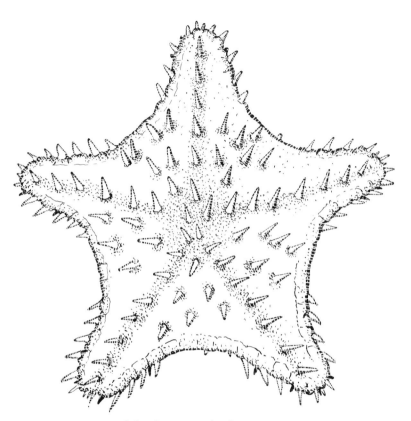

Spiny Sunstar, *Nidorellia armata*

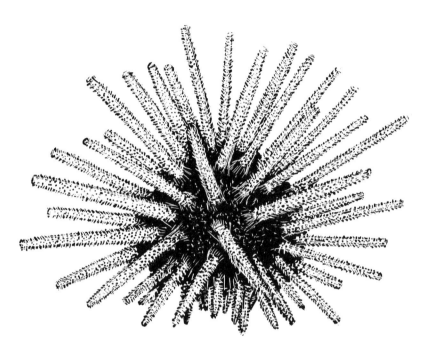

Club-spined Sea Urchin, *Eucidaris thouarsii*

colour well matches particularly its sombre background. The Spiny Sunstar, *Nidorellia armata*, a very variable species, is found from southern California to Ecuador.

Sea Urchins

These animals have the same fundamental five-rayed symmetry and the same strange internal systems as the starfish, although they look very unlike each other. The sea urchin has a globular shell in which all the soft parts are enclosed. The mouth is placed in a depression underneath, whereas the anus is situated on top. During life, the sea urchin is usually protected by a *cheval-de-frise* of spines, sometimes extremely long, sometimes very short, but when the animal dies the spines usually become detached. The sea-urchin shell is often washed up onto the shore and then disintegrates. In the Galapagos, however, whole beaches are made of the spines of one species. This is the Club-spined Sea Urchin, *Eucidaris thouarsii*, which is commonly found around rocky shores of James, Albemarle and Charles and perhaps of other islands.

There is considerable variation in the shape of sea urchins, and in a number of species the body becomes flattened and the spines very numerous and small. These are commonly called cake urchins, or sand dollars or sea-biscuits because when dead the creamy-yellow, flattened disc of the sea urchin has that appearance. Two Galapagos species are *Encope micropora* and *Clypeaster rotundus*. When a sea-biscuit is examined, the five double rows of pores, from which protrude the 'tube-feet' when the animal is alive, can be easily made out. *E. micropora* is known as a 'keyhole' urchin on account of the shape of the perforation.

The rather small sea urchin *Lytechinus semituberculatus* is found washed up on sandy shores. It has beautiful lime-green spines which seem to adhere rather better than in most sea urchin species. Two or three are sometimes the only flotsam to be seen on sandy beaches.

Mollusca

There are over 70,000 species of mollusc and the group is second only to the ARTHROPODA, containing the INSECTA and CRUSTACEA, in the numbers of species. The numbers are usually a measure of

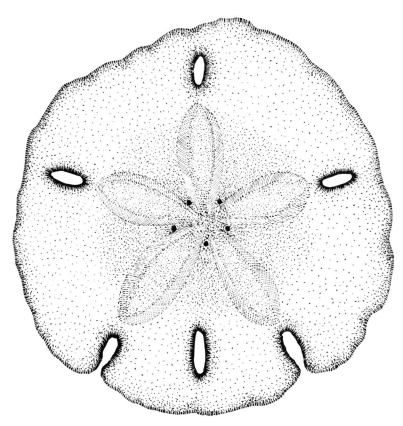

Sea-biscuit, *Encope micropora*

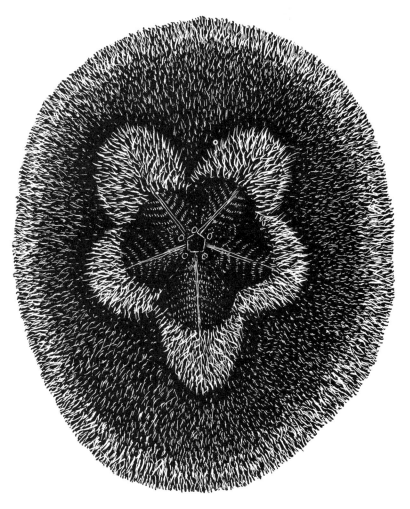

Clypeaster rotundus

Sea Urchin, *Lytechinus semituberculatus*

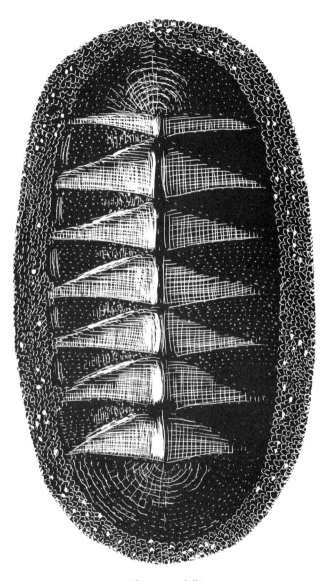

Chiton goodalli

the success of the group in adapting itself to the various niches in nature. Molluscs are soft-bodied (which is the meaning of their name), although a large proportion secrete a hard shell or shells for protection, as otherwise they would be prone to predation. The most primitive molluscs are the chitons. These possess a simple internal anatomy and the head region is reduced. The most characteristic feature is the row of hard wing-like shells, almost always eight in number and overlapping like the tiles on the roof of a house.

A number of chiton species are abundant around the rocky shores of the Archipelago. Some of them are large—at least 10 cm (4 in) in length—and the visitor should have no difficulty in finding them at lower water, fastened on to the rocks. Each chiton moves extremely slowly, browsing over the algae-covered rocks, rasping off vegetable fragments with its radula. This special organ is a ribbon-shaped tongue covered with rows of strong recurved teeth.

One of the common molluscs is *Chiton goodalli* which at four inches (10 cm) in length is large for a chiton. It is almost black in colour, like the water-worn lava slabs near the low-tide mark where it is found sticking so firmly that few predators can remove it. The bleached, bone-like disarticulated valves are a common component of many beaches. There are a number of smaller species.

Gastropoda

This is the largest group of molluscs and includes the snails, slugs, limpets, periwinkles, whelks and many other well known animals; many known only by their shells. In the chitons the much reduced head and the anus are at opposite ends of the body, whereas in the gastropods, due to a twisting of the viscera, the anus lies above the mouth and the head is pronounced. Perhaps the best known gastropods bear a shell which consists of a whorl, the size enlarging the nearer it gets to the aperture. The abundance of the typical gastropod shells', on the beach, and even the living animals themselves in the coastal waters, appears to have undergone a change during the fifty years since Beebe's visit. On Indefatigable he said, 'Here were cones, turrets, conches, glorious murex, chitons and rare coloured cowry shells'. Today one can see small examples of most of these by diligent searching, except for the valves of the chiton shells, but there can be nothing like the wealth of shells that were there in Beebe's time.

The living animals are not plentiful in the shallow water, say the

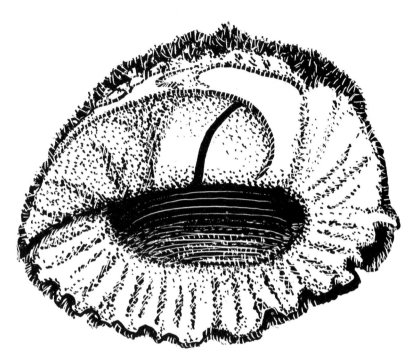

Masked Flat Snail, *Thais planospira*

divers, but species of *Murex* are fairly common, as are Horse-conches with a foot of scarlet with blue spots, although the shell is usually encrusted.

MASKED FLAT SNAIL, *Thais planospira*

Although common, this snail is difficult to find. This is due to the algae and other organisms which attach themselves to the simple limpet-like shell. Underneath, however, it bears a remarkable resemblance to a bloodshot, rather theatrical, eye which Gus Angermeyer described to me as the 'eye of Judas'.

CONE-SHELLS ARE DANGEROUS!

The Cone-shell, *Conus dali*, is illustrated. Cone-shells containing the living mollusc should be handled *with the greatest care* as some species are known to be dangerous, inflicting a painful sting and injecting venom. A number of fatalities are recorded from Cone-shell collecting in the Pacific.

BIVALVES, PELECYPODA

In this group of molluscs, which includes the oysters, scallops, clams and mussels, the foot is shaped like a hatchet and the two shells are joined by an elastic, but horny, ligament. A beautiful scallop, *Pecten magnificans*, is to be found, the mantle of which is orange or red with blue spots. It is usually in rather deep water, 18.5 m (10 fathoms) or so. The hatchet foot of bivalves is used for progression on or in sand or mud which is the situation in which they are normally found.

Cephalopoda—Squid, Octopus and Nautilus

Cephalopoda literally means head-footed because the mantle is divided into a number of limbs or 'arms' and encircles the head. The molluscan shell exhibits several stages of reduction. The Nautilus has a large, but delicate, coiled shell; squids merely possess a calcareous or horny plate embedded in the mantle, whilst the octopus is devoid of any vestige of it. Many species of squid are found in Galapagos waters and a number of them swarm near the surface at night.

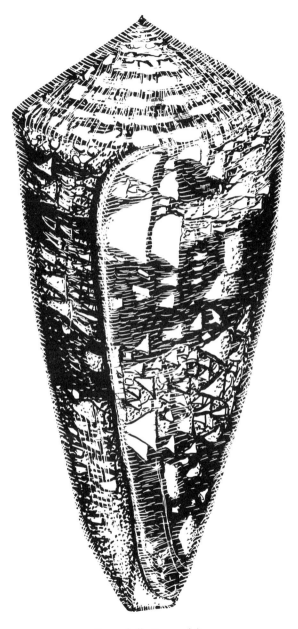

Cone-shell, *Conus dali*

Crustacea—Crabs, Lobsters, Shrimps

One of the main divisions of the ARTHROPODA, the CRUSTACEA share equal status with the insecta, the ARACHNIDA and some other groups of lesser importance. The common character, however, is the possession of jointed appendages either of the head, the thorax, or the abdomen, or the combination of these three main divisions into which the body is generally divided.

Decapoda—Crabs

This important group of the CRUSTACEA is well represented in the Galapagos and no visitor could miss seeing the brilliantly coloured 'Sally Lightfoot' Crab, *Grapsus grapsus*, scrambling over the black lava rocks along the shore. Sometimes they are present by the hundred and often when a photograph is taken of an iguana or some other animal on the shore the Sally Lightfoot is to be seen in the picture. By contrast with the sea-wet, black lava, their scarlet is most vivid and they are extremely agile walking with mincing steps even up vertical surfaces. They are so abundant that they are never out of sight on rocky shores of the Galapagos: yet although widely distributed, being found from Florida to Jamaica, as well as on the Pacific coast of the American mainland, they are never found in such numbers. The young are almost black and appear to run even faster!

A crab found in relatively shallow water, but on rocky shores, is *Mithrax belii*. It possesses a hard, encrusted integument and is often washed up onto the shore intact, until the Lava Gulls see it.

Lobsters—Palinuridea

On the north and west coasts of a number of islands commercial fishing for lobsters takes place. Three species are taken in large numbers although the percentage of each varies tremendously. Two spiny lobsters occur, *Palinurus gracilis* and *P. penicillatus*, and a slipper lobster *Scyllarides astori*. They are caught by diving—traps are not used—and an average catch of 50–100 lobsters per diver per day is made.

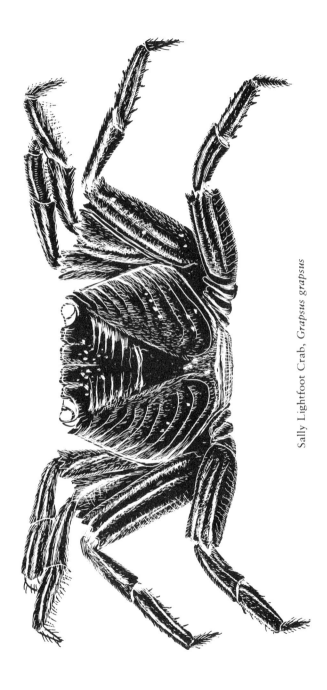

Sally Lightfoot Crab, *Grapsus grapsus*

Barnacles—Eucirripedia

It often comes as a surprise to learn that the barnacles and acorn shells immovably fixed to rocks between tide-marks and to ships' bottoms and harbour piles all over the world belong to the CRUSTACEA. To appreciate this the observer must watch the animals when they are submerged. The carapace is then partly open and the six pairs of filamentous, biramous, thoracic appendages are protruded and make rhythmic grasping movements in order to catch small organisms for food. On a number of beaches, especially on Hood, the skeletal remains of the large acorn barnacle *Balanus tintinnabulum* are scattered about. They are 2·5 cm (1 in) or more in height and in clusters, standing out distinctly on the black lava shore, being cleaming white suffused with a rosy-pink. Charles Darwin wrote *A Monograph of the Cirripedia*, a work which is still consulted for barnacle identification.

Rock-pool Crustaceans

The great majority of crustaceans are small, generally being about the same size as insects to which they are related on account of possessing jointed appendages. But, whereas most insects are terrestrial, most crustaceans are aquatic. An interesting group of small creatures initially associated with fresh water is found in the rock pools well above high-water mark. At the infrequent times when rain falls, and these rock pools fill, the dormant eggs of several crustaceans hatch out. They quickly pass through larval stages and become mature within a few weeks. During this time the water evaporates rapidly under the tropical sun and the concentration of salt increases to such an extent that it would be lethal to most other animal life. Large numbers of eggs are then laid which remain dormant in the dried mud, sometimes for several years. These small crustaceans are known to be carried in dried mud on the feet of birds, and when the latter fly down to a fresh pool the mud washes off and the eggs hatch. The following species were found in small pools of fresh water one month after rainfall at the southern end of Chatham.

Triops longicaudatus, 2·5 cm (1 in) in length, excluding the appendages, is a well known crustacean found in rainwater-filled pools with muddy bottoms. The genus *Apus* with the similar-shaped

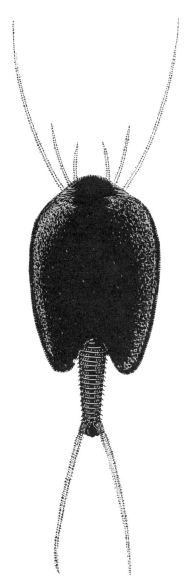

Triops longicaudatus

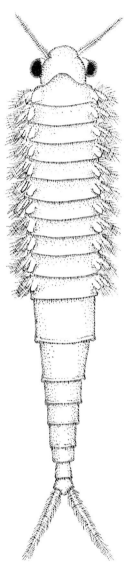

Brine Shrimp of the genus *Cheirocephalus*

carapace is well known to biologists. Brine shrimps are elongated crustaceans which swim on their backs, inhabiting rain-filled rock and mud pools. The eggs are highly resistant to desiccation and heat, and may spend several years as eggs, hatching only when rain has fallen. The specimen illustrated is of the genus *Cheirocephalus* and is from Chatham. It is a female and the male is required for identification of the species.

The OSTRACODA group are usually minute and live inside a carapace which is like a bivalve mollusc. It can close the valves during conditions of stress, but when they are open the jointed appendages, by means of which it swims and presumably obtains nourishment, clearly show its relationship. The species found by Somerhays at Chatham in a rain-filled rock pool was 0·6 cm ($\frac{1}{4}$ in) in length, certainly not minute!

Terrestrial Invertebrates

Spiders—Arachnida: Araneae

This class of the ARTHROPODA includes the scorpions, mites, ticks and harvestmen in addition to the spiders (Order ARANEAE). As Bucksbaum says, no class of animals is 'less loved by most people'. The arachnids of the Galapagos have not received as much attention from biologists as have some other groups, although several writers have mentioned them in their general accounts.

Over fifty species of spiders are found in the Galapagos and Beebe has described the experience of coming across huge *Epeira* spiders with giant grasshoppers and huge sphinx moths caught and mummified in their webs. This is *Epeira oaxensis* which is 2·5 cm (1 in) in length with yellow-orange legs and cream-coloured markings on its dark body. An endemic species, *Lathrodectes apicalis*, lives in crevices in the lava rocks and spins a small sheet or web in front of its tunnel-like home. The legs and cephalothorax are stated to be of dull leaden-brown whilst the abdomen is black in ground colour with a yellow band around the anterior border and three scarlet bands across the abdomen. This is very closely related to the similar species distributed throughout the southern United States and throughout other countries of the world. These are known to harbour venom of lethal effect. Beware of spiders!

In James' Bay between the shore and the lagoon, spiders with large spiny abdomens sling their webs across the paths between the

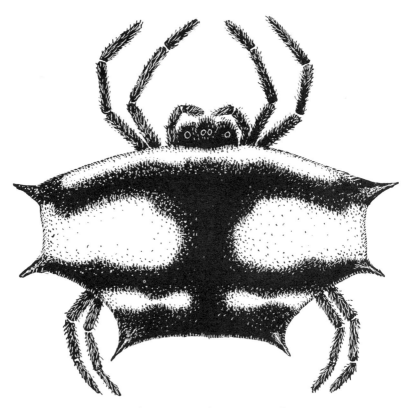

Web-spinning spider *Gasteracantha*

shrubs. From the illustration, the British Museum authorities thought the species was *Gasteracantha servillei* which has been described from the Galapagos.

Chilopoda—Centipedes

Numerous naturalists have mentioned the centipedes of the Galapagos. There are a number of different species, but most attention has been given to the giant, 30 cm (1 ft) long red and black *Scolopendra galapagoensis*.

Centipedes are nocturnal and hide in crevices during daylight, but at least two diurnal Galapagos birds feed on them. These are the Galapagos Hawk and the Culpepper subspecies of the mocking bird. The hawk has been found to have its crop stuffed with the creatures.

Centipedes are members of the ARTHROPODA with poison claws modified from the appendages of the first body segment. A poisonous secretion can be injected through the perforated tips into the prey, all centipedes being carnivorous. The birds which prey upon them do not appear to be troubled by the venom.

CHAPTER 12

Notes for the Visitor

In this chapter notes are given to help the would-be visitor in his travel arrangements, so that he has some idea of what he may expect in terms of weather, facilities and living conditions.

Climate and Weather

The climate of the Galapagos is influenced by their geographical location on the Equator and by the various ocean currents which flow to or through them during the course of the year.

Ocean Currents

The Archipelago lies at the convergence of several major current systems of the Eastern Pacific. This results in a unique variety of marine life, varying from warm temperate to tropical. It also accounts for the rather strange climate of the Islands, which even though they lie on the Equator are classed as subtropical.

The Peru current is a complex system of currents and counter-currents flowing parallel to the coast of South America. The Peru coastal current, also known as the Humboldt, and the Peru Oceanic current both flow northwards and westwards to join the South Equatorial current which flows through the Archipelago. Both currents bring cool nutrient-rich waters up from the Southern Ocean.

Flowing beneath and against the South Equatorial current is the Equatorial counter-current or Cromwell current. This is a sub-marine current which flows from the mid-Pacific eastwards and is deflected upwards by the Islands of Fernandina and Isabela, producing upwellings of cool nutrient-rich waters which help to account for the abundance of marine life in that area.

The fourth major current is the Niño. This is less a current than a flow of warm water from the north, to some extent filling a vacuum caused by the lessening of the flow of the Peru and South Equatorial currents. This warm water comes in the first four months of the year, though in some years it does not appear at all. It generally brings with it hot tropical weather with heavy rain-showers.

The Climate

There are two distinct seasons in the Galapagos, essentially caused by variations in the water temperature, which are in turn to a large extent the result of the movement of the regular wind-systems north and south.

The warm season runs from January to May and may be characterized by heavy rain-showers during part of this time, the water temperatures being in the mid to upper 70s, (25° C.) rising to a high of 85° (30° C.) when the Niño flow is at its height.

The cool or *garua* season starts in late June and runs through November, the chief characteristics of this season being the cooler water, upper 60s and low 70s, (20°–23° C.) the overcast skies and the drizzle showers caused by a temperature inversion and the light to fresh southerly winds which give rise to a rather short choppy sea.

During this season the highlands of the larger islands are often cloud-covered for days or even weeks on end.

Accommodation

There are very few places where visitors can stay in the Galapagos.

In San Cristóbal there are a couple of inexpensive hotels, but not a great deal of interest.

In Floreana there is the *Pension Wittmer* which is comfortable and with excellent food.

Pto. Ayora on Academy Bay, Santa Cruz, is the main tourist centre in the islands. On arrival at the airport on Baltra, visitors with no prior arrangements made will take the bus to South Channel, which separates Santa Cruz from Baltra, then cross in a small ferry and board another bus for the 1 hour (40 km) journey to Pto. Ayora. Here there are 5 hotels.

Hotel Delfin is tied in with a boat-hotel cruise and is not normally available for casual visitors. *Hotel Galápagos*, run by Forrest Nelson, situated right on the Bay, has accommodation for 30 in double cabins with bathrooms. *Hotel Solymar*, run by Jimmy Perez, also situated on the Bay, has accommodation for 24 in double or triple cabins with bathrooms. Slightly less expensive than Hotel Galápagos.

Hotel Colon Insular and *Hotel Pacífico*, located in 'centre of town' are inexpensive and provide the bare minimum.

There are a few 'cottages' available for longer-term occupation and one or two other houses where accommodation may be had inexpensively for a short period. There is a small campsite available for those who prefer.

The water supply in Santa Cruz is brackish and should not be drunk untreated.

Travel

There are at present a number of boats operating for visitors to the islands. There are two large vessels making regular scheduled cruises with 90 passengers—these are the *Santa Cruz* and *Buccaneer*. There is a boat-hotel programme operated by the Hotel Sievers in conjunction with the yachts *Delfin* and *Isabela*—group-size is 16–30.

There are a number of private yachts for charter, ranging from 32 to 70 feet in length; arrangements for all these should be made well in advance. There are also a number of small, 25–35 feet local boats which accommodate 6/8 passengers with minimal facilities; these can be chartered on arrival in Academy Bay. If you are alone or with only one or two other persons, arrangements can often be made with others on the flight out to make up a charter party. The Hotel Solymar operates a day-trip programme based on the hotel. This is often a good alternative for those with no desire to experience life on small boats. Hotel Galápagos may also start a day-trip programme shortly.

M/N *Santa Cruz*: 90 passengers; 5/8-day cruises.
M/N *Buccaneer*: 90 passengers; 5/8-day cruises.

Delfín/Isabela/Hotel Delfín: 30/16 passengers; 3/4/7/10-day cruises.

Yacht *Encantada*, 70 ft schooner: 10/11 passengers; charter and 1 or 2 week cruises.

Yacht *Sulidae*, 63 ft gaff ketch: 10 passengers; charter.

Yacht *Bronzewing*, 46 ft sloop: 5/6 passengers; charter.

Yacht *Tip-Top*, 34 ft cutter: 4/5 passengers; charter.

Yacht *Symbol*, 36 ft ketch: 5/6 passengers; charter.

Yacht *Nixe*, 32 ft cutter: 4 passengers; charter.

Yacht *Tigress*, 57 ft schooner: 6 passengers; charter.

Yacht *La BelleVie* 38 ft TSDY: 6/8 passengers; charter.

For further information contact:

Metropolitan Touring, Casilla 2542, Quito, Ecuador.
  Iguana, Delfín/Isabela/Hotel Sievers.
  Encantada, Sulidae, Bronzewing, Tip-Top.

Gordon Tours Cía. Ltda., Casilla 5284, Guayaquil, Ecuador.
  Buccaneer.

Macchiavelo Tours, Casilla 318, Guayaquil, Ecuador.
  Neptuno.

Fritz Angermeyer, Santa Cruz, Galápagos.
  Nixe.

Carl Angermeyer, Santa Cruz, Galápagos.
  Symbol.

Bernhard Schreyer, Santa Cruz, Galápagos.
  Tigress.

In U.S.A. contact:

Galapagos Tourist Corporation, 888 Seventh Avenue, New York, N.Y. 10019. Tel. 212.582–7373.

Mountain Travel Inc., 1398 Solano Av., Albany, Ca. 94706. Tel. 415.527.8100 for yachts.

Adventure Associates, 5925 Maple, Dallas, Texas 75235. Tel. 800–527–2500.

Hanns Ebensten Travel, 55 West 42nd St., New York, N.Y. 10036. Tel. 212.354.6634.

In ENGLAND contact:

Twickenham Travel Ltd, 22 Church St., Twickenham, TW1 3NW. Tel. 01-892 7606.

In FRANCE contact:

Voile Voyages, 9 Rue Domat, 75005 Paris. Tel. 329.30.30 for yachts.
Odyssee S.A., 137 Rue Du Ranelagh, 75016 Paris. Tel. 288–82–66
for yacht.

In DENMARK contact:

Jorgen Bitsch Safari, APS-Horedganden 33, DK 8410 Rønde, Denmark. Tel. 06–371822 for yachts.

Generally speaking the visitor would be well advised to make
plans and reservations well in advance. Though it is possible to
make arrangements upon arrival, this can result in discomfort,
especially during the busy periods of December, January, June, July
and August and may consume a considerable portion of your time.

There are flights to the islands from Quito via Guayaquil every
Tuesday, Friday and Saturday and some additional flights on Mon-
days, Thursdays and Sundays operated by the larger vessels. Contact Metropolitan Touring for full information on the various
flights, most of which *cannot* be written into your international
ticket.

The National Park Service

The Ecuadorian Government has now established a National Park
Service, operated by Ecuadorians, to run the Galapagos National
Park. With headquarters in Academy Bay, on Santa Cruz, they have
already taken over various programmes, such as goat eradication
and tortoise protection in the wild, from the Darwin Station. They
have established plans for the regulation of the tourist industry and
have made a considerable impact on the islands in the short time
since they started. There is an entry tax, at present $6 but likely
to increase.

The main difficulty is the problem of enforcing the laws and regulations, and to this end the Park Service need the help and coopera-
tion of all visitors whose aim should be the same as theirs—to
preserve and conserve the Galapagos and their unique ecology for
posterity.

Though some of their regulations and arrangements may not
seem perfect to the visitor, be assured that they have the islands
and future visitors at heart.

No natural object may be removed from the islands and visitors are encouraged to pick up any litter they may see. All groups must be accompanied by a qualified guide. Please make every effort to make his job easier by following his directions and instructions. Leave only footprints, take only photographs.

Health

Health requirements are limited to a valid certificate for vaccination against smallpox. However, if travelling elsewhere in South America, inoculation against yellow fever and cholera may be desirable.

A personal first aid kit is never out of place in your baggage although the outfits carried on board the larger ships are fairly comprehensive and most emergencies can be dealt with. There is a hospital at Academy Bay, though this should not be relied on for other than emergency treatment. The strength of the sun is such that anti-sunburn or suntan lotions should be applied liberally and regularly, even during relatively cloudy periods. Self-adhesive plasters may come in useful for blisters and scratches, and embrocation for aching muscles, especially if one is unaccustomed to rough walking. Moleskin or adhesive foam is excellent for blisters caused by shoes and it is often useful to have an antibiotic ointment.

Passport Requirements

United Kingdom passport-holders do not require a visa for Ecuador. United States citizens require a visitor's card issued by the airlines. Regulations are subject to alteration, of course, but your travel agent will advise you.

Clothing

Clothing in Guayaquil is as for any tropical city, but out in the islands there is no use for coats, ties and smart shoes. Luggage should be packed in a soft bag. Cabins are usually small and hard suitcases take up too much room, so cannot be stored aboard. Soft bags are often compulsory. Arrangements are usually made with agents in Guayaquil or Quito for hard cases and other goods not wanted during the visit to the islands to be stored safely until one's return.

When packing on the morning of the flight out to the islands, use your soft bag and pack everything else in your hard cases for safekeeping.

Clothing should be as drip-dry as possible. Laundry facilities are usually scanty or non-existent. Towels and linen may, or may not, be provided depending on your choice of vessel. Liquid detergent is always useful as it can be used in sea water. Fresh water is always at a premium on the boats as it is all transported out from Guayaquil and must be used sparingly.

Experience has shown that the most useful clothing is as follows:

For ladies
   2 pairs light-weight slacks
   1 light-weight dress (optional)
   3 drip-dry blouses (two with long sleeves)
   1 pair ankle-high walking shoes with rubber soles
   3 pairs drip-dry socks
   1 sweater or light-weight parka for the cool evenings
   1 nightdress, or pyjamas
   1 bathing suit
   1 pair shorts
   1 pair rubber-soled slippers, to wear on board
   1 hat
   drip-dry underclothing

For men
   2 pairs trousers (Levis (jeans) are recommended), or if shorts are preferred, at least one pair of trousers
   5 shirts (two with long sleeves)
   1 pair ankle-high walking shoes with rubber soles
   3 pairs drip-dry socks
   1 pair pyjamas
   1 bathing suit
   1 pair shorts
   1 pair rubber-soled slippers, to wear on board
   1 hat
   1 sweater or light-weight parka
   drip-dry underclothing

An extra-heavy sweater when on passage, and for evenings, is a good idea during the *garua* season, from July to early November.

Protection against the sun must be a prime consideration. People used to the sun's exposure elsewhere can suffer even on an overcast day. A good pair of sunglasses is essential.

Swimming

There is plenty of safe swimming but it is unwise to swim alone without informing some responsible person, such as a crew member, or to swim early and late in the day.

Currency

There are often difficulties concerning sterling travellers' cheques in South America, so that it is strongly advised that U.S. dollar travellers' cheques are used.

Wet and Dry Landings

All landings at the various piers, beaches and rocks where visitors to the Galapagos Islands disembark can be looked upon as adventurous in some degree. With the exceptions of the ex-American landing stage at Baltra and that at Academy Bay, concrete landing places are not in good order, usually with concrete slabs badly damaged or washed away. Some are not available at all stages of the tide. They may be completely awash or one might have to wade some distance before it is reached. These points are made so that the visitor may dress accordingly.

Landings may be made at a number of open beaches. This is carried out by swinging over the side of the launch or dinghy at the precise time that the water ebbs down the beach, then scrambling up the beach before the next wave flows in—but it is possible to get wet to the middle. Clothes soon dry, however, in the Galapagos and any discomfort is temporary. Canvas footwear of a type which covers the ankles should be worn for all landings, and if stouter footwear is to be worn for a long walk or lava scrambling, then these should be placed in a bag, as well as cameras, of course. The bag should then be handed ashore by a crew member.

The Charles Darwin Foundation for the Galapagos Islands

This international association was founded under the auspices of UNESCO for the purpose of furthering appropriate scientific studies. This is, in the main, accomplished through the establishment of the Charles Darwin Research Station at Santa Cruz Island with the support of the Government of Ecuador. It was dedicated in 1964.

The aim of the station is to provide facilities for the study of the islands and to advise the National Park Service on steps to be taken for their conservation.

In the first place, facilities are provided for scientists to work at their own projects, which are sponsored elsewhere. The projects undertaken must be authorized by the Foundation as well as by the Government of Ecuador National Park administration. All scientific work on the islands is planned so as not to interfere unduly with the wildlife and, indeed, the Foundation and the National Park administration will permit no field research which could do serious harm to any element of the indigenous fauna or flora.

The next two categories of function with which the Research Station occupies itself concern conservation. It is arguable which is the most important, but the one project with which the Station identifies itself concerns the Galapagos giant tortoise in its numerous island races. It is thought that here is selection being applied by nature and, in spite of the dominant role being played by man by his application of a very heavy selection pressure, as far as possible the latter is held in check. Even though the tortoises of several islands were near extinction, due to Man's influence, directly or through the agency of feral species of his once domesticated ones, the visitor to the Station is first conducted to a tortoisarium where tortoises from the different islands of the Archipelago are reared to the stage where they can be re-introduced to their original habitat, at least in those subspecies where they are most in danger. More recently, scientists at the station have started a Land Iguana breeding programme as a result of the high proportion of Indefatigable Iguanas, that have been killed by feral dogs, results so far have been very encouraging.

The Research Station of the Charles Darwin Foundation is situated at Academy Bay on the south shore of Indefatigable (Santa Cruz). The unobtrusive buildings are located amongst a cactus forest (*Opuntia*) and as one walks along the paths around the low buildings one is not aware that this unique Galapagos forest type has been violated in any way. Look for the minute blue butterflies (*Leptotes parrhasioides*) fluttering around the flowering shrubs and for the Dark-billed Cuckoo (*Coccyzus melacoryphus*). At the Station also are kept a number of tortoises which are thought either to be unique or whose pedigree is not known. The former are protected so that suitable males are sought for them whilst the latter are not released because they might cause genetic impurity to invade the island races.

Further Reading

Stimulated by Darwin's early observations, much has been written about the Fauna and Flora of the Galapagos. In the list of Galapagos references received at the Charles Darwin Research Station there were nearly 70 items up to the end of 1970. However, by far the best bibliography on the Archipelago's natural history is that compiled by Thornton which takes up thirty-four pages. In this present work we give a short list of essential material for the reader who wishes to enquire further, together with a few general accounts of animal groups where the the information is scattered. The specialist should consult either the Charles Darwin Research Station list of references or Thornton's bibliography.

Austin, O. L. *Birds of the World* (1961)

Beebe, W. *Galapagos World's End* (New York, 1924)

Boone, L. 'Galapagos Brachyura', *Zoologica*, NY 8 no 4 (1927)

Boone, L. 'The Littoral Crustacean Fauna of the Galapagos Islands', Part II 'Anomura', *Zoological NY* **14** no 1 (1933)

Brongersma, L. D. *Guide for the Identification of Stranded Turtles on British Coasts* (British Museum [Natural History] 1967)

Brower, Kenneth (ed.). *Galapagos—the Flow of Wildness*, vol 1 'Discovery', vol 2 'Prospect' (San Francisco, 1970)

Buchsbaum, R. *Animals without Backbones* (first published USA 1938). Now available paperback 2 vols

Burt, W. H. & Grossenheider, R. P. *A Field Guide to the Mammals* (Boston, 1952)

Bustard, Robert. *Sea Turtles: Their Natural History and Conservation* (1972)

Carlquist, Sherwin. *Island Life: a Natural History of the Islands of the World* (New York, 1965)

Clark, H. L. Papers from the Hopkins Stanford Galapagos Expedition 1898–1899, 12, 'Echinodermata', *Proc Wash Acad Sci* **4** (1902), 521–32

Cousteau, Jacques-Yves & Cousteau, Philippe. *The Shark—Splendid Savage of the Sea* (1971)

Darwin, C. *Journal of Researches into the Natural History and Geology of the Countries visited during the voyage of H.M.S. Beagle round the world* (1845)

Dyke, Edwin C. Van. 'The Coleoptera of the Galapagos Islands', *Calif Acad Sci Occasional Papers* **22** (1953)

Eibl-Eibesfeldt, I. *Galapagos* (1960)

Editors of *Life* & Barnett, L. *The Wonders of Life on Earth*, Ch 1 (New York, 1960)

Fraser, F. C. *Guide for the Identification and Reporting of Stranded Whales, Dolphins and Porpoises on the British Coasts* (British Museum [Natural History], 1969)

Gifford, E. W. 'Birds of the Galapagos Islands with Observations on the Birds of Cocos and Clipperton Islands (Columbiformes, Pelicaniformes)', *Proc Calif Acad Sci* (4S) **2** no 1 (1913), 1–132

Harrison, P. P. O. *Birds of the South Pacific: a Handbook for Passengers and Seafarers.* (Royal Naval Bird Watching Society, Narberth, 1962)

Hayes, A. H., 'The Larger Moths of the Galápagos Islands (Geometroidea: Sphingoidea and Noctuoidea)', *Proc Calif Acad Sci* **XL**,(7), 145–208 (1975)

Holthuis L. B. & Joesch, H. 'The Lobsters of the Galapagos Islands (Decapoda, Palinuridea)', *Crustaceana* **12** no 2 (1967), 214–22

Hult, J. 'Crustacea Decapoda from the Galapagos Islands collected by Rolf Blomberg', *Ark Zool* **30A** no 5 (1938), 1–18

King, Judith E. *Seals of the World* (British Museum [Natural History], 1964)

Lack, D. *Darwin's Finches* (1947)

Linsley, E. C. & Usinger, R. L. 'Insects of the Galapagos Islands', *Proc Calif Acad Sci* (4S) **33** no 7 (1966)

MacFarland, C. 'Giant Tortoises, Goliaths of the Galapagos', *National Geographic* **142** no 5 (1972)

McBirney A. R. & Williams H. 'Geology and Petrology of the Galapagos Islands', *Mem Geol Soc Am* **118** (1909)

McIntosh, E. & Balfour, D. *Islas Galapagos. Notes on Anchorages. Discover Galapagos* (Guayaquil, Ecuador, n.d.)

Norman, J. R. (revised by Greenwood, P. H.) *A History of Fishes* (second edition, 1963)

Peterson, R. T. 'The Galapagos Eerie, Cradle of New Species', *National Geographic* **131** no 4 (1967)

Rosenblatt, H. R. & Walker, B. W. 'The Marine Shore Fishes of the Galapagos Islands', *Tenth Pacific Science Congress of the Pacific Science Association, Hawaii* (1961)

Sivertsen, E. 'Littoral Crustacea Decapoda from the Galapagos Islands', *Meddr zool Mus, Oslo* **38** (1933)

Slevin, J. R. 'The Galapagos Islands: A History of their Exploration', *Calif Acad Sci, Occasional Papers* (1959)

Sparks, J. & Soper, T. *Penguins* (Newton Abbot, 1967)

Steinbeck, J. & Ricketts, E. F. *Sea of Cortez* (New York, 1941)

Thornton, I. *Darwin's Islands. A Natural History of the Galapagos* (New York, 1971)

Townsend, C. H. 'The Astor Expedition to the Galapagos Islands', *Bull NY Zool Soc* **33** no 4, 134–71

Vries, T. de. *The Galapagos Hawk. An eco-geographical study with special reference to its systemic portion.* (1973) Thesis presented to the Free University of Amsterdam

White, Alan & Epler, Bruce. *Galapagos Guide* (Quito, 1972)

Wiggins, I. L. & Porter, D. M. *Flora of the Galapagos Islands* (Stanford, California, 1971)

Wittmer, M. *Floreana* (English translation 1961)

Zuber, Christian. *Animal Paradise* (1964)

INDEX

Scientific names are shown in italics
Italic numerals indicate illustrations

Abingdon (island), 21
Acanthoderes galapagoensis, 191
Accommodation, 219
Actitis macularia, 92
Aetobatus narinari, 123, *124*
Agassiz, A., 19
Agassiz expedition, 19
Agraulis vanillae galapagoensis, *161*, 162
Agrius cingulata, 171, *173*
Albatross (US ship), 19
Albatross, Waved, 66, 67
Albemarle (island), 21
Amblyrhynchus cristatus, 109, *110*, *111*
Anas bahamensis, 61, 62
Anas discors, 93
Angel fish, white-banded, *133*
Anoplura, 154
Anous stolidus, 81
Ants, 193
Apterygota, 143
Arachnida, 215
Arctidae, 176, *177*
Arctocephalus australis galapagoensis, 33, *34*
Arcturus (ship), 20
Arenaria interpres, 91
Asio flammeus, 55, 58

Bahamas Pintail, 61, 62
Balaenoptera borealis, 39, 40
Balaenoptera physalis, 37, 38
Baltra (island), 21

Barnacles, 212
Barn Owl, 59
Barrington (island), 21
Bat-fish, 137, *138*, *139*
Bats, 24
Beagle (HMS), 18, 19
Beebe, Willam, 19, 20
Bees, 193
Beetles, 183
Bindloe (island), 21
Bird Lice, 154, *155*
Black Rail, 60
Black Rat, 24
Blattaria, 149
Bobolink, 96
Bolivia (island), 21
Boobies, 70, 71, *73*
Booklice, 154
Bos taurus, 25
Bottle-nosed Dolphin, 43, *44*
Bubulcus ibis, 61
Buff-backed Heron, 61
Buteo galapagoensis, 50, *51*
Butterflies and moths, 159
Butterfly-fish, 132

Calasoma galapagoensis, 183, *185*, *186*
California Academy of Science Expeditions, 19, 20
Canis canis, 26
Capra hircus, 27
Carcharinus albimarginatus, *120*, *121*
Carcharinus maculipinnis, 118, *119*

Carcharodon carcharias, 121
Casmerodius albus, 89
Cat, 24
Catoptrophorus semipalmatus, 94
Cattle, Domestic, 25
Centipedes, 217
Cephalopoda, 208
Cetorhinus maximus, 123
Charadrius semipalmatus, 91
Charles Darwin Foundation, 226
Charles (island), 21
Chatham (island), 21
Cheesman, E., 19
Cheirocephalus sp., 214, 215
Chelonia mydas, 104, 105, 106
Chilomyctenus sp., 127
Chilopoda, 217
Chiton goodalli, 205, 206
Cicindela galapagoensis, 183, 184
Climate, 218, 219
Clothing, 223
Clypeaster rotundus, 201, 203
Coccyzus melacoryphus, 59
Cockroaches, 149, 150
Coleoptera, 183
Collenette, C. L., 19
Colnett, Capt., 20
Conolophus spp., 105, 107, 108
Conus dali, 208, 209
Cormorant, Flightless, 76, 77
Cornelius Crane Pacific Expedition, 20
Cowley, Ambrose, 20
Crabs, 210
Crickets, 144, 148
Crocethia alba, 91
Crustacea, 210
Cryptotermes brevis, 152, 153
Cuckoo, Dark-billed, 59
Culpepper (island), 21
Curio, E., 20
Currency, 225
Cynthia carye, 164, 166
Cynthia virginiensis, 162, 163

Danaus gilippus, 166, 167
Danaus plexippus, 165, 166
Darwin, Charles, 18
Darwin Foundation, 226

Darwin (island), 21
Darwin Memorial Expedition, 20
Darwin's Finches, 61, 63
Dassigney (island), 21
Dean (island), 21
Decapoda, 210
Delphinus delphis, 43, 45, 46
Dendroica petechia, 55, 57
Dermapterna, 149
Deutsche Galapagos Expedition, 20
Devil-fish, Giant, 125, 126
Dictyoptera, 149
Diomedea irrorata, 66, 67
Diptera, 195
Dog, Feral, 26
Dolichonyx oryzivorous, 96
Dolphin, Common, 43, 45, 46
Domestic Cattle, 25
Donkey, 26
Dove, Galapagos, 52, 53
Dowitcher, Short-billed, 94
Dragonflies, 143
Dromicus spp., 116
Duncan (island), 21

Eagle-Ray, Spotted, 123, 124
Earwigs, 149
Echeneis naucrates, 135, 136, 137
Echinodermata, 197
Egret, Common, 89
Egret, Snowy, 93
Eibl-Eibesfeldt, I., 20
Encope micropora, 201, 202
Erinnys ello encantada, 175, 176
Erolia minutilla, 92
Española (island), 21
Estola galapagoensis, 188
Eucidaris thouarsii, 200, 201
Eucirripedia, 212
Eugenie (frigate), 19
Eulamia galapagoensis, 123

Falco peregrinus, 93
Fernandina (island), 21
Field Museum of Natural History, 20
Finches, Darwin's, 61 et seq., 63
Fish, 118
Fitzroy, Capt., RN, 18

Flamingo, American, *49*
Flamingo, Galapagos, 48
Flea, Rat, 24
Flies, 195
Floreana (island), 21
Flycatcher, Large-billed, 55
Flycatcher, Vermilion, *55*, *56*
Fregata minor, *69*, 70
Frigate Birds, 68, *69*

Galapagia solitaria, 149, *151*
Galapagos Blue Butterfly, 166, *168*
— Dove, *52*, *53*
— Flamingo, 48
— Fritillary, *161*, 162
— Fur Seal, 33, *34*
— Hawk, *50*, *51*
— Martin, 59
— Penguin, 77, *78*, *79*
— Pintail, 61, *62*
— Sea Lion, 28, *29*, *30*, *31*, *32*
— Sulphur Butterfly, 159, *160*
Galeocerdo arcticus, 123
Gallinula chloropus, 60
Gallinule, Common, 60
Gasna (island), 21
Gasteracantha sp., *216*, 217
Gastropoda, 206
Geckos, 113
Genovesa (island), 21
Geochelone elephantopus, 98, *99*, *103*
Geometridae, 181
Gerandino (island), 21
Gersteckeria galapagoensis, *192*, 193
Gifford Pinchot Expedition, 20
Gil (island), 21
Globe-fishes, 125
Goat, 27
Grande (island), 21
Grapsus grapsus, 210, *211*
Grasshoppers, 144, *146*, *147*
Greagus furcatus, *81*, 82
Gryllus assimilis, 148
Guerra (island), 21
Gulls and Terns, 80

Haematopus palliatus, 89
Hahua-Chumbi, 15

Halobates micans, *158*, 159
Hammerhead Shark, 121, *122*
Hancock Galapagos Expedition, 20
Hans Haas Expedition, 20
Harrison Williams (ship), 19
Hassler (steamer), 19
Hawk, Galapagos, *50*, *51*
Hawk Moths, 171, *172*, *173*, *174*, *175*
Health 223
Heliaster cunningii, *197*, 198
Heller, E., 19
Hemiptera, 157, *158*
Herald (HMS), 19
Herons, 86, *88*
Hesperiidae, 169
Heterodontus quoyi, 123
Heteroscelus incanus, 91
Himantopus mexicanus, 87
Hirundo rustica, 95
Holocanthus passer, 132, *133*
Hood (island), 21
Hopkins Stanford Expedition, 19
Hyles lineata florilega, 171, *172*
Hymenoptera, 193

Iguanas, 105
Illyria (yacht), 20
Indefatigable (island), 21
Insects, 141
Invertebrates (other than Insects), 197
Isabela (island), 21
Islas Encantadas, 16
Isoptera, 152, *153*

James Bay, 17
James (island), 21
Jervis (island), 21

Killer Whale, 40, *42*
Kingfisher, Belted, 95

Land Birds, 48
Land Iguana, 105, *107*, *108*
Landings, 225
Larus fuliginosus, 81
Larus pipixcan, 92
Las Huéfanas, 16
Lasiurus spp., 24

Laterallus jamaicensis, 60
Lee, L. A., 19
Lepidoptera, 159
Leptostylus galapagonensis, 189, 190
Leptotes parrhasioides, 166, 168
Limnodromus griseus, 94
Liparoscelis cooksoni, 144, 147
Lizards, 112, 114, 115
Lobsters, 210
Locusts, 144, 145
Longfield, C., 19
Lytechinus semituberculatus, 201, 204

Mallophaga, 154, 155
Munduca rustica galapagensis, 171, 174
Manta birostris, 125, 126
Manta Ray, 125, 126
Mantodea, 149, 151
Marchena (island), 21
Marine Iguana, 109, 110, 111
Marine Invertebrates, 197
Martin, Galapagos, 59
Martin, Purple, 95
Mary Pinchot (yacht), 20
Megaceryle alcyon, 95
Melichthys ringens, 131, 132
Melipotis harrisoni, 179, 181
Melipotis indomita, 178, 181
Migrant birds, 90
Mocking Birds, 53
Mola mola, 128, 129
Mollusca, 201, 205
Monarch Butterfly, 165, 166
Mouse, House, 25
Mus musculus, 25
Myiarchas magnirostris, 55
Myopsocus chelatus, 156

Nannopterum harrisi, 76, 77
Narborough (island), 21
National Park Service, 222
Naucrates ductor, 132, 134
Nautilus, 208
Neoconocephalus triops, 146
Nesomimus spp., 53, 54, 55
Nidorellia armata, 199, 201
Nina-Chunbi, 15
Noctuidae, 176, 178, 179, 180

Noddy, Brown, 81
Noma (yacht), 19
Norfolk (island), 21
North Seymour (island), 21
Norwegian Zoological Expedition, 20
Nourmahal (ship), 20
Numenius phaeopus, 91
Nunez (island), 21
Nyctanassa violacea, 87, 88

Ocean currents, 218
Octopus, 208
Odonata, 143
Ogcocephalus darwini, 137, 138, 139
Olmedo (island), 21
Orcinus orca, 40, 42
Orthoptera, 144
Oryzomys spp., 23
Osprey, 93
Owls, 55
Oxydia lignata, 181, 182
Oystercatcher, American, 89

Palinuridea, 210
Pandion haliaetus, 93
Pandora (HMS), 19
Passport requirements, 223
Pentinopygus mannopteri, 155
Pelican, Brown, 83, 84
Pelicanus occidentalis, 83, 84
Penguin, Galapagos, 77, 78, 79
Peregrine, 93
Peterel (HMS), 19
Petrels and Shearwaters, 85
Phaeton aethereus, 74, 75
Phalarope, Northern, 91
Phalarope, Wilson's, 92
Phalaropus pobatus, 91
Phalaropus tricolor, 92
Phoebis sennae marcellina, 159, 160
Phoenicopterus ruber, 48, 49
Physeter catodon, 40, 41
Pig, Feral, 26
Pilot-fish, 132, 134
Pinta (isand), 21
Pinzón (island), 21
Plata (island), 21
Plaza islets, 21

Plovers, 90, 91
Porter (island), 21
Post Office barrel, 17
Praying Mantids, 149, *151*
Prionurus laticlavius, 129, *130*
Progne modesta, 59
Progne subis, 95
Psocoptera, 154
Puffer Fish, 126, *127*
Pyrocephalus rubinus, 55, 56

Queen Butterfly, 166, *167*

Rábida (island), 21
Rail, Black, 60
Rat, black, 24
Rat Flea, 24
Rattus rattus, 24
Remora, *135*, *136*, 137
Reptiles, 97
Rhinacodon typus, 121
Rice Rats, 23
Riparia riparia, 95
Rock-pool Crustaceans, 212
Rorqual, Common, 37, *38*

St. George Expedition, 19
San Cristóbal (island), 21
Sanderling, 91
Sandpipers, 92, 93
San Salvador (island), 21
Santa Cruz (island), 21
Santa Fé (island), 21
Santa Gertrudis (island), 21
Santa María (island), 21
Santiago (island), 21
Schistocerca melanocera, 144, *145*
Sea and shore birds, 66
Sea-Bisquit, 201, *202*, *203*
Sea lions and seals, 28
Sea Urchins, 197, 201, *203*, *204*
Sei Whale, *39*, 40
Seymour (island), 21
Seymour (North and South islands), 21
Sharks, 118, *119*, *120*, *122*
Short-eared Owl, 55, *58*
Skipper Butterflies, 169
Snakes, 116
Snodgrass, R. E., 19

South Seymour (island), 21
Sperm Whale, 40, *41*
Spheniscus mendiculus, 77, *78*, 79
Sphingidae, 171, *172*, *173*, *174*, *175*
Sphyrna lewini, 121, *122*
Spiders, 215, *216*
Squid, 208
Squatarola squatarola, 90
Starfishes, 197
Sterna fuscata, 83
Stilt, Black-necked, 87
Sucking Lice, 154
Sula dactylatra, 72, *73*
Sula nebouxii, 70, *71*
Sula sula, 72
Sun-fish, *128*, 129
Surgeon-fish, 129, *130*
Sus scrofa, 26
Swallow, Bank, 95
Swallow, Barn, 95
Swimming, 225

Tattler, Wandering, 91
Teal, Blue-winged, 93
Templeton Crocker Expedition, 20
Termites, 20, 152, *153*
Tern, Royal, 94
Thais planospira, *207*, 208
Thalasseus maximus, 94
Torres (island), 21
Tortoises, 98, *99*, *103*
Tower (island), 21
Townsend, C. H., 19
Travel, 220
Trigger-fish, *131*, 132
Tringa flavipes, 94
Tringa melanoleaca, 94
Tringa solitaria, 93
Triops longicaudatus, 212, *213*
Tropic Bird, Red-billed, 74, *75*
Tropidurus spp., 112, *114*, *115*
Turnstone, Ruddy, 91
Tursiops truncatus, 43, *44*
Turtle, Green, *104*, 105, *106*
Tyto alba, 59

Urbanus dorantes galapagoensis, 169, *170*

US National Museum, 20
Utethesia ornatrix, 176, 177

Valdez (island), 21
Velero III (R/V), 20
Vincent Astor Expedition, 20
von Hagen, Wolfgang, 20

Warbler, Yellow, 55, 57
Washington Academy of Science, 19
Wasps, 193
Watkins, Patrick, 17
Weather, 218
Weil's disease, 24
Wenman (island), 21
Whales and Dolphins, 36
Wheeler, William Morton, 19
Whimbrel, 91

Willet, 94
Williams, F. X., 19
Wolf (island), 21

Xarifa (yacht), 20
Xenopsylla cheopis, 24

Yellow-crowned Night Heron, 87, *88*
Yellowlegs, Greater, 94
Yellowlegs, Lesser, 94
Yellow Warbler, 55, 57
York (island), 21

Zaia (schooner), 20
Zale obsita, *180*, 181
Zalophus californianus wollebackii, 28, 29, 30, 31, 32
Zenaida galapagoensis, 52, 53